BENGALI HOUSEHOLD TALES

BENGALI HOUSEHOLD TALES

Volume I

COLLECTED AND TRANSLATED
BY
WILLIAM McCULLOCH

Rupa . Co

First published by Hodder and Stoughton, 1912
This reprint in Rupa Paperback 2002

Published by
Rupa & Co.
7/16 Ansari Road, Daryaganj
New Delhi 110 002

Offices at:
15 Bankim Chatterjee Street, Kolkata 700 073
135 South Malaka, Allahabad 211 001
P. G. Solanki Path, Lamington Road, Mumbai 400 007
36, Kutty Street, Nungambakkam, Chennai 600 007
Surya Shree, B-6, New 66, Shankara Park,
Basavangudi, Bangalore 560 004
3-5-612, Himayat Nagar, Hyderabad 500 029

ISBN 81-7167-703-7

Printed in India by
Saurabh Print-O-Pack, A-15-16, Sector-IV,
Noida 201 301

Contents

ABBREVIATIONS USED IN THE NOTES

CAS . 'Santal Folk-Tales,' by A. Campbell, D.D.
CLER . 'Eastern Romances and Stories,' by W. A. Clouston.
CLP . 'Popular Tales and Fictions,' by W. A. Clouston.
FOD . 'Old Deccan Days,' by M. Frere.
GHT . 'Grimm's Household Tales,' tr. by Mrs. Hunt.
GOS . 'Sicilianische Marchen,' gesammelt von L. Gonzenbach.
HGA . 'Griechische and Albanesische Marchen,' gesammelt von J. G. v. Hahn.
HSF . 'The Science of Fairy Tales,' by S. Hartland.
KKT . 'Folk-Tales of Kashmir,' by the Rev. J. Hinton Knowles.
KRS . 'Sagen und Marchen der Sudslaven,' von F. S. Krauss.
KSS . 'Katha-sarit-sagara,' tr. by C. H. Tawney.
LDB . 'Folk-Tales of Bengal,' by the Rev. L. B. Day.
MBH . 'Mahabharata.'
MCF . 'The Childhood of Fiction,' by J. A. MacCulloch.
MWR . 'Religious Thought and Life in India,' by Monier Williams.
RRT . 'Russian Folk-Tales,' by W. R. S. Ralston.
SIF . 'Indian Fairy Tales,' by M. Stokes.
Sk. . Sanskrit.
STT . 'Tibetan Tales,' by F. Anton v. Schiefner, tr. by W. R. S. Ralston.
TYT . 'Yule-tide Stories,' by Benjamin Thorpe.

I

KARMASUTRA[1]

Once upon a time, in a certain village, there lived a Bhattacharya[2] Brahman. He possessed a son, a daughter, a wife, and a cow, and was a very learned man. One night, he was lying awake, when everybody else in the house was sound asleep. All at once, he happened to notice a thread hanging down from one of the rafters. While he looked at it, it grew longer and thicker, till, at length, he saw that it was not a thread, but a huge snake.[3] Immediately on his seeing the snake, he sprang up in alarm, but, while he was in the very act of rousing his wife and children, the snake bit all three of them, and they died the same moment that

---

[1]On the irresistible power of *Karma, i.e.,* the inevitableness of fate, cf. KKT, 326 ff.

[2]Lit. a revered teacher. The students of the *tols*—native institutions for the study of Sk. literature—address their teachers as Bh. The word is used as their family surname by the highest of the Kulin Brahman sects in Bengal. The proper occupation of a Bh. is that of pundit or of family priest to high-caste people.

[3]Cf. LDB, p. 101. In the dead of night, an almost invisible thread comes out of Swet Basanta's wife's left nostril and thickens into a huge snake. Also, KKT, pp. 421 ff. A deadly black snake descends from the sky to slay the sleeping king.

they were bitten. Then the snake glided quickly away.

In great grief and agitation, the Brahman said to himself: "What shall I gain by remaining here any longer?" So saying, he went off in the same direction as the snake had gone. As soon as he was outside of the house, he saw the snake making for the cow-shed. The Brahman hurried after it. When he got to the shed, no snake was to be seen, but a huge tiger bounded past him, carrying off the cow.

In great fear, the Brahman now left his house altogether, and set out to go to the forest.[4] Just as he was coming near the skiirts of it, day dawned. The Brahman, worn out with grief and with walking most of the night, now lay down to sleep at the foot of a tree. A little while after, he awoke, and saw, standing before him, a Brahman. Looking up at him, he asked, "Who are you?" The old man, in turn, asked him, "Who are you?" The Brahman answered, "I am so-and-so. Being in great grief because, last night, my wife and children were killed by a snake and my cow carried off by a tiger, I have left my house and wandered hither. But who are you?" The aged Brahman answered, "I am that snake and that tiger." Hearing this, the Brahman started up and said, "Then, how are you now a Brahman? What is your name?" The stranger answered, "My name is Karmasutra. I appear in various shapes, and roam about all over the world. Whatever kind of death is to befal each man, I bring it about." Then the Brahman said, "My son, daughter, wife, and

[4]*Viz.*, to abandon the world and lead the life of an ascetic.

cow—you killed them all. Why did you not kill me too?" Karmasutra answered, "Your death is not to be in that way. In the water of the Ganges, where it is deep enough to reach your neck, your death will take place. There, an alligator will carry you off." Saying this, the aged Brahman disappeared. The other determined to set out at once, and not to stop travelling till he should come to a country where there was no lake or river at all. For two or three months, he journeyed on, and, at length, arrived at a great city. There a powerful Raja dwelt. It happened that, on the very day the Brahman arrived a great festival was being held in that Raja's house. Now, from the time he commenced his travels, the Brahman had never enjoyed even one good meal.[5] In the hope that, here, at last, he would get one, the Brahman went to the Raja's palace, and stayed there as a guest. The Raja paid him all due respect and ordered his servants to make ready food for him. The command was no sooner given than everything was ready, and the Brahman, having bathed and performed his daily devotions, went away to cook his food.[6]

It happened that, at that time, a great many very holy pundits were gathered together in the palace. In

[5]A serious matter for a professional Bhattacharya, with whom attendance at feasts—where a big feed of dainties as well as a *dakshina* or donation is obtained—is one of the chief businesses of life.

[6]*Viz.,* his rice. Sweetmeats, etc., prepared by a *modok* or *moira* he could eat, but not rice, cooked by a person of low caste. Now a-days, well-to-do Bengalis often keep Brahman cooks, so as to be able to show hospitality to people of any caste, however high.

their assembly, various scriptures were being discussed. The newly-come Brahman, being, himself, a very learned man and hearing a scriptural discussion going on, left his cooking, and began to take part in it. In a very short time, he vanquished all the others in argument, and gained the first place in the assembly. So greatly was the Raja delighted with his learning that he appointed him to be his own court-pundit.[7]

For a time, the Brahman lived there in the greatest happiness. Not very long after he came, a son was born to the Raja. The Raja put the boy under the care of the court-pundit, and, within a short time, the pundit had instructed him in many sciences.[8] When the prince reached the age of thirteen or fourteen, the Raja took it into his head to remove with his court to the banks of the Ganges. On hearing this, the Brahman came to him, and said, "Moharaj, if you are going to live on the banks of the Ganges, then allow me to depart. For I am resolved not to go near the banks of the Ganges." The Raja, much surprised, asked, "What is your reason?" Then the Brahman said, "Moharaj, I am sure to lose my life if I go to the banks of the Ganges,

---

[7]A somewhat satirical account of the King of Gaur's court-pundit will be found in B. C. Chatterji's 'Mrinalini,' pp. 42 ff.

[8]In the Introduction to the 'Hitopadesa,' Vishnusarman undertakes to teach the princes Policy in six months. Twelve years is the period allotted by rule to Grammar, "the gate to all knowledge." Sarvavarman offers to make King Satavahana master of it in six months, and, by the grace of the god Karttikeya, is enabled to keep his word—KSS, I, pp. 39 f.

therefore I will not go there." When the Raja heard this, he began to hesitate a little, but the prince cried, ""If the Brahman does not go, then I will not go; he must be taken along with us." So the Raja said to the Brahman, "Do come, reverend sir; there, I will do whatever you wish." The Brahman, seeing there was no help for it, agreed to go along with the Raja and his court.

When they arrived at the Ganges, the Raja caused a splendid palace to be built on the river-bank. There he lived for some time in great happiness along with all his family and court. The young prince was passionately fond of his Brahman tutor. Wherever he went, he would have the Brahman to accompany him; otherwise, he could in no way be persuaded to go anywhere. One day, he said to the Raja, "Father, I wish to bathe in the Ganges." "Very well," replied his father, "you may do so"; and, at once, he gave ordered to his servants to conduct the prince to the Ganges that he might bathe. Everything was got ready, and the company was just about to set off, when the prince saw that the Brahman was not among his attendants. He at once went to the Raja and said, "Unless the Brahman goes with me, I will not bathe in the Ganges." The Raja sent to call the Brahman, and, when he came, told him to go along with his son to bathe in the Ganges. The Brahman answered, "Moharaj, I have already said that I will not go into the water of the Ganges, for, if I do so, an alligator will devour me." The Raja then said to the prince, "Go you and bathe alone." But the boy would not hear of going, unless the Brahman went with him.

Still the latter was unwilling to go, and still the prince insisted that he should. At length, the Raja said, "Reverend sir, pray go; I will provide against all danger." Saying this, he gave orders to his servants to surround with a net the place where his son and the Brahman were to bathe, and to stand ready with their weapons, in great numbers, both on the land and in the water. He commanded them, also, to form a ring all round the Brahman, when he went down into the river.[9]

The Raja's orders were at once carried out, and then the prince and the Brahman went down to the water, and entered it where it was very shallow. The attendants stood all around, as the Raja had commanded. Gradually, the Brahman's fear passed off,[10] and, at length, little by little, he went farther and farther in, till the water reached up to his neck. Instantly upon this, the boy said to him, "Thakur, I am no prince; I am Karmasutra!" Still saying this, he took the form of an alligator, and, seizing the Brahman, went off with him in a moment.

---

[9]But all in vain. For, "however well guarded, what is smitten by Fate, perishes"—'Hitop.' II, 18.

[10]He forgot the need of caution. For, "when disaster has drawn nigh, the minds of men often becomes obscured"—'Hitop.' I, 27. But no care would have availed now. For "when Fate descends, caution is in vain"—'Anwari Suhaili,' I, 19, quoted in CLER, p. 566. "*Niyatih kena badhyate*"—who (or what) can resist Fate?—is a very common expression of condolence with a friend in Bengal, when a dear relative has died. It is the ending of a Sk. *sloka:*
"Matulo yasya Govindah, pita yasya Dhananjayah,
So' bhimanyu rane sete, niyatih kena badhyate."
"Though Krishna was his uncle, and Arjuna, his father.
Yet Abhimanyu lies low on the battlefield. Who can resist Fate?"

II

THE BRAHMAN AND THE KAYASTHA[1]

In a certain village, there once lived a Brahman and a Kayastha. The Brahman was very religious, truthful, and just. He would never do any work whatever, without, first of all, offering the daily worship enjoined by the Sastras. The Kayastha, on the other hand, was a most impious and wicked man. He was always in some way or other mocking at the Brahman. He would say to him, "You do pious works, and yet can get nothing to eat. But, look here; I drink and do all kinds of wicked deeds, and yet I want for nothing." The Brahman bore all his taunts, without answering him one word.

One day, the Brahman happened to go to bathe in the Ganges. While he was bathing, a sharp stake ran into his foot, and much blood began to flow. He would have fallen down, but many people, crowding round,

[1]Kayasthas, variously described in the Sastras as Kahatriyas and as Sudras, appear to have been originally the clerk and accountant class. In the Bengal of to-day, they form a numerous, highly respectable and advanced community, able to admit themselves to be Sudras without much disadvantage, since, except in point of formal caste, they are quite abreast of the Brahmans. See J. N. Bhattacharjee, 'Hindu Castes and Sects,' pp. 175 ff.

held him up, and led him out of the water. Then the poor Brahman, with great pain and difficulty, began to try to make his way home. At that very time, the Kayastha chanced to pass along that way, and met with the Brahman. When he heard of his misfortune, he said, "See here; your life is most holy and pious; you diligently perform all religious ceremonies; and yet, to-day, you have all but met your death; while I, this same day, have found this bag of gold coins. Which way of life is the more profitable, then, your or mine?"

The were still talking, when an astrologer chanced to come up. They both asked him what was the cause of their strange fates. Then the astrologer, having by careful reckoning ascertained the truth, said: "Brahman, in a former life, you were a great sinner. You were guilty of Brahman-murder, cow-murder, and many suchlike awful crimes. Accordingly, it as ordained in your destiny that, to-day, you should be impaled. But, in this life, you have done, and are always doing many holy deeds; therefore, instead of impalement, you have suffered only this punishment to-day. And you, Kayastha, in a former life, were exceedingly pious. You did many holy and righteous deeds; and, as a reward for all those, you were to have been made a Raja to-day. But, in this life, you have done, and are still doing wicked deeds without number; therefore, instead of being made a Raja, you have got only that bag of gold pieces which you found today." The Brahman and the Kayastha, having heard the words of the astrologer, returned to their homes.

III

THE BRAHMAN'S LUCK

Once on a time, there was a very poor but uncommonly learned Brahman. He had studied all the Sastras, till he was profoundly versed in them, but had no means whatever of earning a livelihood. His wife was constantly saying to him, "Bamon,[1] your books of astrology and suchlike rubbish are never out of your hands, day or night; but you never once consider how people's stomachs are to be kept going." "Bramhoni,"[2] he used to reply, "what good will my considering to? If the Giver does not give, all my efforts will be in vain. And, more than that. At present, I'm under the influence of Shoni.[3] So there's not the

[1]Vulgar colloquial for *Bramhon,* as Benglis pronounce the Sk. *Brahmana.*

[2]So Bengalis pronounce Sk. *Brahmani.* Hindu husband and wife never address each other by name. The wife will, on no account, even speak of her husband by name.

[3]The planet, Saturn, Sk., *Sani.* He is caled *Krura-dris* and *Krura-lochana,* "the malignant-eyed," because his influence is more disastrous than that of any other planet. See LDB, p. 108 ff., 'The Evil Eye of Sani'; he casts his eye on Sribatsa for three years, and, during that time, Lakshmi, the goddess of good fortune, with all the will in the world, is almost powerless to help him. Cf. CLER, p. 231: "The entrance of Saturn into the Brahman's horoscope turned

slightest possibility of my securing an income anywhere. On the contrary, whatever I take in hand, bad luck is sure to dog my steps." Don't speak to me about your books of astrology and your Shonis," his wife would retort. "You're too lazy to be willing to stir out of the house. That's why you can earn nothing." Then the Brahman would say, "You're only a foolish woman. So it's natural for you to think in that way. You don't look to the future. If only you can be comfortable for the present, you think nothing more is needful. So it's useless to argue with you about such things. Of course, as you're my wife, it's my duty to support you, and, naturally you can't help feeling aggrieved, when you have to suffer want; I don't blame you for that. But what can I do?" "What can you do?" rejoined he Brahmani on the occasion. "Surely there's no lack of Rajas in this country, and many of them are open-handed enough. Can't you go to some of them, and see what's to be got?" "It won't be of the slightest use," said the Brahman. "Even if they treat me with all due respect—nay, lay themselves out to show quite exceptional regard for me—I shan't be a single pice the better off for all that. I've made a reckoning by the stars, and know for certain that there's another six

---

everything upside-down." It has to be remembered that the planets are regarded as personal being—"machtige Herrscher," as Gunkel calls them. See CLER, p. 264, Note; also, p. 374.

[4]Cf. Shah Manssur, who is persistently unlucky till his luck changes once for all. CLER, pp. 12-45. Also, Sadullah, to whom Kasharkasha gives only trifling help again and again, until what befalls him in

months' poverty and hardship before me."[4] "Confound your reckonings and you too," cried his wife. "Believing those astrological books of yours, you'll sit still for another six months, will you? And then, I daresay, you'll just have to go out and fetch home a shipful of riches to the *ghat!*"[5] This was rather more than the Brahman could stand. He got up in a huff and said, "Very well. I'll go at once. You'll see how much'll come of it."

So he got his old, shabby clothes well washed, and started off for the nearest Raja's palace. He was an old man, and there was a long way to go. It took him some four days to reach the place. The Raja was just going out to bathe, when the Brahman appeared, and gave him his blessing. He received the old man with the utmost respect, requested him to be seated, and asked, "Thakur, to what do I owe the honour of this visit?" The Brahman answered in verse to this effect: "Your Majesty, I am come to lay a complaint before you. Constrained by your mighty power, poverty and distress have fled from your city, hotly pursued by your munificence, which has followed close at their heels, like an officer of justice. In mortal terror of him, and

---

connection with that, shows that his luck has turned—*ib.,* pp. 94 ff. Cf. *ib.,* pp. 109, 112, and 480 ff., specially 481 f. "Misfortunes are contagious," says the king. "I had heard of your ill-luck and dared not receive you into my palace again, fearing that your ill-luck should affect me and put it out of my power to assist you when your star should look more favourably on you." See, also, the story of Shoayb; *ib.,* p. 129. That is the case of a man whose ill-luck persists to the end. With it, cf. RRT, pp. 197 ff.

[5]Landing-place, or steps down to a river or tank for bathers.

finding no other refuge, the criminals have hidden themselves in my humble cottage. I have, therefore come to-day to inform your Majesty." The Brahman's words surprised and delighted the Raja beyond measure. "Thakur," said he, "many Brahman pundits visit me, but not one of them have I ever heard recite such beautiful verses. I'm filled with admiration of your learning and cleverness. What sort of present is fit to be given to such a man as you?" Now, the Raja happened, as has been said, to be on the point of going to bathe, and so was holding in his hands the big and little copper pots for making libations of water to the spirits of his dead parents.[6] A happy thought struck him. He held out the two pots to the Brahman, and said, "Thakur, take these. They're the things I, myself, use. I can't think of any other gift befitting such talents and accomplishments as yours." The

---

[6]This is the kind of *Sraddha*—rite performed for the benefit of a deceased parent or ancestor after he had become invested with his intermediate body—called *nitya, i.e.,* daily or regular. See MWR, pp. 274 ff., 303 ff.

[7]"Say, *Hari, Hari!*" Sk. *Hari* is one of the names of Vishnu, popularly etymologized to mean "the remover of sin"—and, therefore, of calamity. "*Horibol Hori!*" is a very common ejaculation when anything disastrous or disappointing happeans. The bearers keep repeating it, when taking a corpse to the burning-ghat. So a man says, "*Radhe-Madhob!*" or "*Ram! Ram!*" when anything he disapproves is proposed to him, and on similar occasions. Such "repetitions" of a divine name are by no means "vain." The mere sound possesses a wonderful efficacy. Thus a robber-captain is said to have attained salvation at death, because, when professionally employed, he used constantly to shout "*Mar, mar!*"—*i.e.,* "Strike, strike!"—to his men—*mar* being only *Ram* inverted.

Brahman was dumbfounded. "Horibol Hori!"[7] said he to himself. "Didn't I tell the Brahmhoni over and over again that, do what I might just now, I should only have my labour for my pains? But the hussy wouldn't listen to me. And, now, how's an old man like me to make that four days' journey home? How am I to get food on the way?" Revolving all this in his mind, he gave the Raja his blessing, and took his departure.

With no small difficulty and hardship, the Brahman managed to make his way back to his home, where his wife was looking out for him in a state of high hope and expectation. What splendid gifts would he not bring? "Well, how did you get on? What have you got?" was her greeting to her husband, as soon as he appeared. "What have I got?" he retorted. "I've got more than enough. You'll not need to want any more for food and clothing." "Why, what has happened?" she asked. "What else should happen?" said he. "I've got such a grand gift as the Raja would give to no other man. I've received the very highest honour he could confer on me. And"—holding out the pots—"this is what it all amounts to." It was too much. For once in her life, even the Brahmani could find nothing to say adequate to the occasion.

Some weeks passed. The Brahmani's spirit gradually revived, and she began again, "Though you didn't get anything the very first place you went to, that is no sort of reason why you shouldn't try somewhere else. People have got to make one effort after another, dear knows how often. If, positively, everything possible has been done, yet nothing has come of it all, then, of course, it's plain that Fate's against them."[8] "There you are at your nagging again," said the Brahman. "How often am I to explain to you that, for the present, my destiny contains nothing good—nothing but fruitless labour?" "Oh," she replied, "you go just once again—just once. I hear that, in yonder country, there's a Raja whose generosity is unbounded, and there's nobody he show such favour to as Brahman pundits. You pay him a visit. Something good is sure to come of it, and we shall be relieved of our poverty once for all." Her husband said, "Brahmhoni, you're an incorrigible fool. But, as your one aim in life is to make me take fruitless trouble, there's nothing for me but to go."

Once more, the Brahman's old *dhuti* and *chhador*[9] got a good washing; then, taking a palmyra-leaf umbrella and a bamboo staff, he began his journey.

---

[8]"Lakshmi comes to the lion-like man who exerts himself; it is poltroons who say 'Fate must give.' Striking down Fate, act manfully in thine own strength. When an effort has been made, if souccess does not follow, there is, then, no blame"—'Hitop.,' Introd., 31. "Works are accomplished by exertion, not by wishes; deer, assuredly, do not enter the mouth of the lion when he is asleep"—*ib.,* Introd., 36. Cf. *ib.,* II, 4; also, CLER, pp. 121 ff. and 137. The king declares his view that good fortune depends on character, wisdom, and diligence; but, what happens in the case of Shoayb, convinces him that he has been mistaken.

[9]A Bengali's usual dress consists of the *dhuti*—a long strip of muslin, wound round the limbs and waist—the *piryan*—a white cotton shirt—and the *chhador*—an oblong piece of muslin, which may be worn scarf-wise over the shoulders or wrapped round the upper part of the body. Old-fashioned villagers wear only the first and the last.

After several days' severe toil and hardship, he arrived at the palace. It was a building of huge size, with a lofty lion-gateway,[10] before which many armed sepoys were standing on guard. Nobody could enter but by their leave. When the Brahman tried to do so, he got such a push back that he fell sprawling on the ground.[11] He painfully picked himself up again, and said to the man that had pushed him, "Sir Sepoy, please let me pass; I must get audience of the Raja." "A seedy old dotard like you get admission to the Raja!" was the reply. "You just clear out, and look sharp about it." The Brahman said, "I'm a Brahman and, though I'm poor, I'm not a dotard. Have the kindness to let me pass." But the sepoys would not listen, and only made fun of him. He was sitting there in great distress, quite at a loss what to do, when an old durwan[12] chanced to come out of the palace. The Brahman told him all his story. Feeling rather sorry for him, the old durwan said, "Well, Thakur, you wait here. I'll go and tell the Raja. He has given strict orders that nobody is to be admitted to his presence without being announced." "Very

---

[10]Sk., *sinhadvara*. Cf. *sinhasana* = throne. Formerly, the main entrance to a palace and the king's seat in his darbar hall were always adorned with figures of lions.

[11]The story seems to assume that the sepoys were Musalmans. They are represented as speaking Musalmani Bengali. Hence, their disrespectful treatment of the Brahman. Contrast the Hindu king's behaviour.

[12]Durwans—gatekeepers—in Bengal, are often up-country Brahmans. Such are, of course, regarded as much lower in caste than Bhattacharjis and the like.

good," was the reply. "You go and tell the Raja. I'll wait here till you come back." The old durwan went inside and said to the Raja, "Your Majesty, a Brahman is seeking admission to your presence." "A Brahman? Then fetch him in at once," answered the Raja. "And take good care that not the slightest disrespect is shown him." In obedience to the Raja's command, the old durwan went to the lion-gate, and called to the Brahman, "Come along, Thakur, come along." The Brahman, gathering up his umbrella and staff, was on the point of entering, when one of the sepoys called out, "You mustn't take all that trash with you." The poor Brahman, shaking with fear, set down his umbrella and staff at the gate, and then followed the durwan into the Raja's presence.

As soon as he saw the Brahman enter his hall of audience, the Raja jumped up from his throne, and, when he approached, prostrated himself before him,[13] and then gave him a seat in an honourable place. when the Brahman was seated, the Raja asked him, "Thakur, do you carry on any business?" "Yes," he replied. "Though I'm a Brahman, I carry on the trade of a potter." "What?" said the astonished Raja. "You, a Brahman, carry on the trade of a potter![14] What on earth do you mean?" "Listen, your Majesty," answered

---

[13]He made what is known as a *sashtanya* obeisance—a prostration such that all eight (*ashta*) members of the body (*anga*), the hands, breast, forehead, knees, and feet, touch the ground.

[14]The trade of potter was and is an impossibly low-caste occupation for a Bhattacharji Brahman.

the Brahman in verse. "My soul is like clay. That clay is moistened with the tears of my starving wife and children. With that moist clay, I frame many, many vessels, namely, hopes. And my destiny is ever shattering these vessels. Therefore I say that, though I am a Brahman, I have had to take up the trade of a potter." The Raja was greatly charmed with such a beautiful verse. Never in all his life, had he heard anything equal to it. "Thakur," said he, "thanks to your blessing,[15] many pundits are in the habit of visiting me, but none of them has ever recited such a wonderful verse as this. Never once have I met a man of such amazing ability as you. I can't tell you how pleased I am with you! I wonder what I should give you as a reward. It won't do to insult you by offering the sort of things I give to the common ruck of pundits. Really, I can't think of anything in my possession that is fit to be presented to you." Saying this, he sat in silence, thinking for a while. Then, suddenly getting up from his throne, he embraced the Brahman with great fervour, and said, "Thakur, I can think of nothing else fit to be given to such a scholar as you, so I give you my own bosom." The gift of the Raja's bosom quite took away the Brahman's breath. Fairly flabbergasted

[15]A very common formula of politeness. You ask a man, who never saw you before, some question about himself or his family. "By your blessing, such-and-such is the case," he replies. When a European visits an out-of-the-way village, the people come to him with all sorts of petitions. *E.g.*, "Shaheb, the water we get to drink, *by your blessing* isn't very good. Couldn't you graciously induce the Sarkar to dig us another tank?"

as he was, however, he somehow managed to give the Raja his blessing in due form, and made his exit. When he reached the gateway, his umbrella and stick were nowhere to be seen. He asked the sepoys about them, but they told him roughly to shut up. Were they set there to look after his rubbish? At this, the poor Brahman could no longer keep back his tears. How was he to make the journey home? His umbrella and staff, the only things he had to help him, even these were now gone. Thinking sadly on his evil luck, he took the road home, and, begging his way, after much suffering, arrived in sight of his house. The Brahmani had no fears that her husband would return empty-handed this time. So, as soon as she saw him coming, she ran to meet him, and eagerly asked, "Well, Thakur, what have you brought?" "Oh, I've brought plenty," was the reply. "Come away inside, and I'll let you see." Hearing this, the Brahmani felt surer than ever that he must have brought something very fine. She hurried back into the house, followed by her husband. The moment he got inside the door, he clasped his wife to his bosom so vigorously that she screamed, "Oh! oh! What are you doing? Let me go! Let me go!" Her husband said, "Why, what are you going on about? I'm giving you what I got." "What do you mean?" said she. "Just what I say," was the reply. "Now you see all I got. Didn't I tell you that, for the present, my destiny holds nothing of any use for me? The Raja did honour enough to my learning. He gave me what no other pundit ever got—his own bosom, as he said. I mean, he embraced me, as if I were his dearest friend. But, as for cash, not a single pice did he give me."[16] The Brahmani was terribly put out. She hadn't a word to say.

At length, the six months came to an end, much to the Brahmani's joy. "Now, Thakur," said she, "those confounded six months are past. You're no longer under Shoni's evil eye. Now's the time for another visit to the Raja." "You're quite right, my dear," was the reply.

---

[16]Cf. CLER, 489 ff. An unfortunate merchant, urged by his wife, resorts unwillingly to the king for help. The king gives him a large quantity of gold coins, but, by way of sparing his dignity, puts them inside a melon. The merchant, supposing what he has got to be only a melon, gives it away, and is thus not a penny the better by his visit to the court. Incited by his wife, he goes again, and the king gives him another melon full of money, which he bestows upon a beggar, and, thus, a second time, gets no pecuniary benefit from the royal kindness. In RRT, p. 157, an unlucky man twice receives ten roubles, which his wife gives away, not knowing what she is doing. His luck turns with the gift of two farthings, which he give to a fisherman. Cf. the story of Hassan Alhabbal, the rope-maker, in the 'Thousand and One Nights,' and the variant of it in TYT, pp. 460 ff. In KSS, I, pp. 515 ff., thrice over, the king Lakshadatta presents a cirtron filled with jewels to his needy dependent, Labdhadatta, who gives it away, supposing it to be merely a citron, and, thus, it comes back to the king. But, when the same gift is again bestowed on Labdhadatta on the fourth day, it slips from his hand and breaks as he is receiving it. The Hindu explanation of such a course of events is that, "until a suitor's guilt, which stands in his way, is removed, a king, even though disposed to give, cannot give; but, when a man's guilt is effaced, a king gives, though strenuously dissuaded from doing so; this depends upon works in a previous state of existence." For, mighty as they are, even the planets are absolutely subservient to Karma. Cf. KSS, I, p. 259.

"I'm certain to gain something worth while by going now." The Brahmani was overjoyed. "Well, Thakur," said she, "now that the planets are favourale to you, no matter what you do, it'll turn out well. You use often to say, yourself, that, when one's stars are favourable, even if he does wicked deeds, they bring him good.[17] So, this time, when you go to the Raja, don't try to please him with flattery and the like. Rather abuse him well, and let's see what your planets will bring out of that for you." "That's the very thing to do," he replied. "Nay, let me once get admitted to the Raja's presence, and not only will I not flatter him, I'll thrash him with my stick."

Saying this, he proceeded to get his clothes and so forth ready, just as on the previous occasions. Then, having determined by astrological recknoning an auspicious day and hour[18] for visiting the Raja, he started on his journey. When he reached the palace gateway, the old durwan who had introduced him before, was sitting there. He had seen with his own eyes with how great deference the Raja had received the old Brahman. So, this time, as soon as he asked for an audience, he at once most respectfully led him into the royal presence. As before, the Raja, on seeing a Brahman enter, very courteously advanced to meet

---

[17]So, the attempts of enemies to injure him are said to turn to the advantage of the man fated to be fortunate—CLER, Note on p. 147.

[18]A most important precaution. So, when Somadatta resolves to start cultivation, he is careful to ascertain a lucky day on which to go to the jungle to look out a plot to clear—KSS, I, p. 153.

him, when the Brahman, without a word, rushing up to him, struck him such a blow on the chest with his stick that the Raja staggered backward four or five paces, and fell all his length on the floor. The courtiers were furious with rage at the Brahman's strange behaviour. The guards drew their swords—another moment, and it would have been all up with the Brahman. But the planets were now exceedingly favourable to him. Seeing what would naturally result from the Brahman's mad action, they caused the roof of the hall, exactly over the spot where the Raja had stood when the Brahman struck him, to fall in with a tremendous crash.[19] Thereupon the Raja, overjoyed at his miraculous escape, with all haste ordered the guards to sheathe their swords, and cried out to the Brahman, "Thakur, never, so long as I live, will I forget the service you have done me to-day. I owe my life to you." Then, turning to the bystandars, he said, "Don't you see, if the Brahman hadn't given me such a push the very moment he came in, the roof would have fallen on me and killed me? If, instead of shoving me, he had only warned me, that would have been of no use. I mightn't have believed him, or, even if I had, I mightn't have got quickly enough out of the way of the falling roof. Thus, you see, the Brahman did the very wisest thing

[19]Cf. FOD, p. 83; also, LDB, pp. 41 and 43—the minister's son saves the prince and his wife from a similar danger. In the 'Madanakamarajankadai,' a minister's son, warned by the conversation of two brids, carries his master asleep out of his tent, just before a huge branch falls upon it and crushes it. Cited in CLP, I, p. 245. Cf., also, CLER, pp. 431 f.

that he could." The Raja's words made them feel rather ashamed, and they all begged the Brahman's pardon for the disrespect they had shown him. The Brahman accepted their excuses with great amiability, and gave the Raja his blessing. The latter had not till now recognized him. When he knew that his benefactor was the same pundit whose learning and poetical ability had made such an impression on him, his joy was redoubled. "I never met a pundit anything like so clever and learned as you," said he. "Besides, I shall be in your debt as long as I live. This kingdom is as much yours as mine. You must remain at my court."[20] The Brahman was only too glad to agree to this proposal. Forthwith, the Raja made every sort of provision for him on the most magnificent scale. Materials were collected and workmen summoned to build him a splendid mansion. Whole potfuls of rupees were sent off to his house. And the Raja in person, surrounded by his retinue, escorted the Brahman home in the grandest style. This sudden change of fortune far surpassed even the Brahmani's wildest expectations. Seeing her husband return with such pomp and state, she was almost beside herself with joy, and listened with wondering delight to the Brahman's account of his adventure. And the favour of the Raja enabled the old couple to pass the rest of their lives in perfect comfort and happiness.

---

[20]Cf. the catastrophic suddenness and completeness with which the luck of Nassar changes—CLER, pp. 141 ff.

III

THE BRAHMAN WHO SWALLOWED A GOD

There lived in a certain place, so the story goes, a Brahman and his wife. The Brahman was very poor, and was doomed by a singular fate to this perpetual trouble, that, when he had eaten half his rice, somethng or other always occurred to interrupt him, so that he could eat no more.[1]

One day, an invitation to the Raja's house came to the Brahman. He thereupon said to his wife: "Half my rice is all I can ever eat: never once in my whole life has my hunger been satisfied. To-day, I've chanced to get this invitation to the Raja's house; but how am I to go? My clothes are dirty, and, if I go a shabby-looking sight, most likely the durwan will turn me out." Hearing this, his wife said, "I will clean your clothes; then you shall put them on and go." So she took and rubbed his clothes with *qhar*,[2] and, having thoroughly cleaned

---

[1]"Stopped when one's rice is only half-eaten" is a proverbial expression in common use. Cf. "Ashes in one's rice, when it is served up," a saying employed in much the same way as our "Many a slip 'twixt the cup and the lip."

[2]Sk., *kshara* = any alkali, such as soda or potash.

them, gave them back to him. The Brahman put them on, and started for the Raja's house. As he was an old and feeble man, it was almost evening before he arrived. When he did get there, he saw that the Brahmans' feast was over. But the Raja, seeing the Brahman come, saluted him very respectfully, and ordered his servants to give him a good dinner. Immediately a great many people set about attending to the Brahman, and he, having found a convenient place, soon cooked and served up his dinner.

As he viewed the dishes of various dainties spread out before him, the Brahman was greatly delighted. He thought to himself, "To-day, at any rate, I will eat my fill." He then sat down and began eating. Now, it happened that, on a beam of the roof, there was a little earthen pot hanging. Just as the Brahman had half finished his dinner, that pot broke, and some of the pieces fell into his food.[3] He immediately drank a

[3]The narrator stated that very strictly living Brahmans may eat rice only once in the day. This seems to be at variance with Medhatithi's comment on Manu, II, 56, according to which two "regular meals" are allowed—one in the morning and one in the evening. Such, at any rate, is present-day custom. Probably, the falling of the fragments of the pot into the food would be held to pollute it. In any case, for a strict Hindu to resume eating after an interruption is out of the question. That would involve the eating of leavings. Speaking on the part of the eater is enough to constitute an interruption. See B. C. Chatterji's 'Durgeshnandini,' pp. 50 ff A mischievous woman tricks a simpleton of a Brahman into speaking and afterwards beginning to eat again, and then threatens to tell people. Similar instances of "providential" baulking of people when wishing to eat, may be found in SIF, pp. 227 ff. In 'Raja Harichand's Punishment,' the plums on a tree move out of his reach; a fish leaps out of a pot into the river; pigeons fly away out of the pot, and maggots fill their place.

little water,[4] got up and washed his hands and mouth, and went to the Raja did him much reverence, and said, "Thakur, are you fully satisfied?" The Brahman answered: "Moharaj, there has been no want of respect and attention to me. My own destiny is to blame that I have not fared well." "Why," said the Raja, "what has happened?" The Brahman replied: "Moharaj, in the room where I was sitting at food, a litle earthen pot was hung up. Suddenly, it chanced to break and spoiled my rice." On hearing this, the Raja became very angry, and gave his servants a scolding. Then he said to the Brahman, "Sir, wait you here to-night; to-morrow, I will give you food with my own hands." The Brahman consented, and remained that night in the Raja's house. Next day, the Raja, having himself made all the preparations, told the Brahman to eat. In the place where he went for his dinner this time, there was nothing by which his rice could possibly be spoiled. To-day, therefore, the Bahman sat down to eat, greatly rejoicing. But, when he had got half through his dinner, Bidhata[5] saw that he must be stopped, and yet he could not seen any means of interfering. At last he, himself,

---

[4]Sk., *gandusha.* The drinking of a little water out of the hand before and after a meal, by way of rinsing the mouth, is a prescribed ceremony, which must on no account be omitted.

[5]In Sk. literature, Vidhata is a name of Brahma, as Creator, or of Visvakarman. But, popularly, by Vidhata Purusha—Bengali, Bidhata Purush—is understood the divinity that fixes beforehand a person's lot in life. In 'Life's Secret'—LDB, pp. 9 ff,—a sister and niece of Vidhata's figure.

took the form of a golden frog[6] and, coming to the edge of the Brahman's plantain leaf, tumbled into his food.

The Brahman, being too busy to notice anything, ate up his rice, frog and all.[7] Dinner over, the Raja asked him, "How now, Thakur? Have you been satisfied to-day?" The Brahman answered: "Moharaj, never since I was born have I dined so well." Saying this, he prepared to take his leave. The Raja gave him, also, some rupees,[8] which the Brahman joyfully accepted, and set off at once for home. After a while, evening came on, as the Brahman was walking through the midst of a jungle. Suddenly, he became aware of a voice saying, "Brahman, let me go! Brahman, let me go!" The Brahman looked all round about, but could see nobody. Again the voice was heard, "Brahman, let me go." Then he said, "Who are you?" The answer came, "I am Bidhata Purush, Bidhata Purush!" The Brahman replied, "Where are you?" Bidhata answered, "You have swallowed me." "Impossible!" said the Brahman. "Yes," said Bidhata. "In the form of a frog, I tumbled into your food, and you ate me up." "Nothing could be better," replied the Brahman; "you've bothered me all my life, you rascal, I'll not let you go! I'll close

---

[6]Said by the narrator to be so called from the colour of its back.

[7]On "Swallow" stories, see MCF, pp. 47 ff. The subject of "Der verschlungene Gott" is very fully treated in Hans Schmidt's 'Jona.'

[8]The donation—*Sk., dakshina*—which all the Brahmans invited to such a feast receive.

up my throat rather!"[9] Bidhata, in great fear, said again, "Brahman, let me go! I'm being stifled!" But the Brahman hurried home as quickly as he could, and, when he arrived, he said to his wife: "Give me a seat and a hookah, and you hold a stout stick ready in your hand." His wife did so at once, and the Brahman, sitting down, smoked straight on, taking care at the same time not to set Bidhata free. The god was nearly stifled, but the Brahman quite disregarded all his entreaties.

Meanwhile, in Heaven and Earth and the infernal world, there was a terrible commotion. All living things were on the point of dying for want of food. The universe was on the eve of collapsing.[10] Then all the gods, having assembled in council, resolved that one of them must be sent to the Brahman. But who was to go? After a second deliberation, they all besought Loqhi[11] to go. She said, "If I go to that Brahman, I shall never come back." But, alas! what could she do? So she yielded to their prayer, and departed to the Brahman's house. Arriving there, she stood at the door, and called loudly on the Brahman, who, on learning that it was Loqhi who called, put his cloth round his

---

[9]Brahmani in alvo demersus deus, per aliam viam descendens, evadere conatus est. Decoris causa, in hoc loco fabulam paululum mutavi.

[10]Cf. the difficulties which arose when Death got "treed" by "Gambling Hansel"—GHT, I, p. 323—and shut up in a sack, in the Bohemian Tale—CLP, I, pp. 387 f.

[11]Sk., *Lakshmi*, wife of Vishnu, the goddess of good fortune, and the ideal of beauty. The last syllable of Loqhi is nasalized.

neck.[12] He invited her to be seated, and asked her what, in the name of wonder, had brought her to a poor man's house. "Thakur," said Loqhi, "you have taken Bidhata a prisoner, and are keeping him. Let him go, or the universe will be ruined." "Give me the stick," said the Brahman to his wife, "and I'll show you what sort of a goddess of good fortune this Loqhi is. From the day I was born, I have enjoyed nothing but bad luck, and now Loqhi comes to my house, forsooth!" Hearing this, the goddess vanished, trembling with fear. She told the gods what had happened, and, after another consultation, they sent Shorosh'oti.[13]

When Shorosh'oti reached the Brahman's house, she called out loudly, "Brahman, are you in? Brahman, are you in?" The Brahman saluted Shorosh'oti with great respect, and said, "Mother, what do you want in a poor man's house?" "Thakur, the universe is fast going to destruction; let Bidhata go." The Brahman burst into a great passion, and cried, "Wife, give me the stick! I will teach this goddess of learning. Even the first letters of the alphabet are oxflesh[14] to me.

---

[12]The *chhador* is put over the back of the neck, with the ends hanging down over the shoulders in front, in sign of revenence or supplication.

[13]Sk., *Sarasvati,* wife of Brahman, goddess of speech and learning.

[14]The most impossible of all foods for a Brahman, the merest external contact with which would be a terible disaster. The popular story is that the great Tagore family of Calcutta owes its present condition of *Pirali*-hood to its high-caste Brahman ancestors' having been made to smell roast beef in the time of the Nawabs. The Brahman means to say with all possible emphasis that he possesses no learning whatever.

Shorosh'oti comes to my house, does she?" Hearing this, the goddess at once made off, stumbling and getting up again in her hurry.

Finally, Sib himself undertook the mission. Now the Brahman was a Soibo,[15] so zealous, too, that, without doing *puja* to Sib, he would not touch even water. As soon, therefore, as the god came, he and his wife, having given him water to wash his feet, and presented an offering of *bel*[16] leaves, holy grass,[17] flowers, sun-dried rice, and sandal wood,[18] did *puja* to him. Sib then sat down, and said to the Brahman, "Brahman, let Bidhata go." The Brahman answered, "As you have come, of course I must let him go, but what am I to do, myself? I have suffered affliction from the day of my birth, and this Bidhata here is the cause of it all." Then Mohadeb[19] said: "You need not trouble yourself on that account; you will go with your body[20] to heaven." Having got this promise, the Brahman relaxed his throat and opened his mouth, and Bidhata came out.[21]

---

[15]Sk. *Saiva,* an adjective formed from the noun *Siva,* denoting the sect which regards Siva as the Supreme Being.

[16]Sk., *vilva,* the tree *Aegle Marmelos,* the leaves of which are an essential in the *puja*—ritual worship—of Siva.

[17]Sk., *durva.*

[18]The water, etc., formed the *arghya,* a reverential oblation made to gods and venerable men.

[19]Sk., *Mahadeva* = great god, Siva's most usual designation.

[20]*Viz.,* without dying. Such "translation" is a most signal mark of divine favour.

[21]Deo permissum est ut per anum Brahmani ex alvo evaderet. Cf. Note 11.

Thereafter, Mohadeb taking the Brahma and his wife along with him, went away back to heaven.

A person's being swallowed and afterwards emerging little or none the worse from inside the swallower, is a favourite Folk-tale *motif* all over the world. Mrigankavati is swallowed by a Rakshasa and emerges uninjured four times a month—KSS, II, p. 291. A beautiful maiden comes out of an elephant—*ib.*, II, p. 488. See also *ib.*, Ii, p. 605, and II, pp. 597 f. A great ship, full of people, is found in a huge fish when it is cut up—*ib.*, II, p. 599. In 'Pride Abased,' a fish swallows the king, who is afterwards cut out alive, but in rather poor condition—KKT, p. 158. See also, CLP, I, pp. 403 ff.

IV

THE BRAHMAN'S VERSE

In a certain village, there lived a very poor and ignorant Brahman. He had the greatest difficulty in getting a living. Indeed, so completely from hand to mouth did he live, that, any day he failed to obtain alms, he had to fast altogether, and, as if such a fortune were not sufficiently hard to bear, he had a wife whose tongue made him dread even to enter his house. What with this trial and his poverty together, the poor man was quite at a loss what to do or where to turn. Day and night, the virago kept harping, "Just see how many Brahman pundits go to the Raja's house, recite a verse or two, and are rewarded with money enough to keep their wives and children in comfort, while you, like the utter good-for-nothing that you are, sit idling in the house, or, when you do go begging, bring in the most wretched pittance. There are hundreds of ways of mending our fortunes, but you can't see them because you don't wish to." "What ways?" answered the Brahman. "I'm quite illiterate, myself. How, then, am I to compose a verse? And I'm not well acquainted with any pundit. So, how am I to get a verse from somebody else, which I may pass off as my own?" "Very well," cried his wife, snatching up her broom, "if you can do nothing, clear out!"

The poor Brahman made off, but, once out, where was he to go? He could think of no place of refuge, so, for a while, he walked on, without caring whither. At length he came to a large garden, and there sat down at a tree-foot. As he sat, he kept racking his brains how to improve his condition, but no possible way could he think of. In the midst of his ponderings, a pig happened to come to that place, and, as pigs usually do, began to flounder in the tank and then come up and rub her body against a tree, time about. For a while, the Brahman watched her in silence. Suddenly, a brilliant idea struck him, and he cried out, "I have it! I've made a verse at last."So saying, he rose up, got a palmleaf,[1] and wrote:

"Rubbing rubbing, dipping, then rubbing with might and main
What your rubbing's all for, is easy enough to explain!"

When he had written this, the Brahman said to himself, "Now, shall I go to the Raja and recite my verse, and see what Destiny has in store for me? Why not? Who knows what he mayn't give me as a reward?" Having come to this resolution, he set off at once.

It was evening when he reached the palace; the time of audience was over for that day, and the Raja had retired to the Rani's apartments. His attendants, too,

---

[1]Children still learn to write on palmyra leaves, in out-of-the-way villages in Bengal. The "infants" carry, each, a quantity of them wrapped in the little square grass mat they take to school to sit on.

had all gone off to their own quarters, so the Brahman could find nobody to tell his errand. As he waited about, he began to get rather nervous. "Likely enough, when he hears my verse, the Raja will order me a beating instead of giving me a present," he thought to himself. "I'll run no such risks I'll not read the verse, but just leave it about somewhere, and see what comes of it." Accordingly, he sought out the place where the Raja was in the habit of sitting when he was getting shaved, and, there hanging up the palm-leaf with his verse on it, hurried away home; but it was very late when he arrived. His wife began abusing him as usual, but he said, "What are you scolding about now? I've written a verse and left it at the palace. Just wait and see. Tomorrow you'll be made a Rani." "You may stop your jokes," she retorted, "nobody here wants them. But this is just like you,—an empty stomach, and a head stuffed with nonsense." "I'm perfectly serious," said he. "I did write a verse, and left it at the Raja's. The court had been dismissed, so I could not see him to-day; but, to-morrow, he can't fail to notice my verse. And won't he be delighted with it? We shall have no more trouble after that. Why, you shall be made a Rani at the very least."

Next morning came, and the Raja, getting up, washed his hands and face, and then went and sat down in the place where he used to be shaved. The barber was already there, busy stropping his razor.

Now, the Rani and Kotwal[2] had plotted together to

[2]The Chief of the police.

murder the Raja, but nobody had courage to attack him openly. So, at length, the Rani sent secretly for the barber and said to him, "To-morrow, when you shave[3] the Raja, cut his throat with your razor. You shall receive an immense reward, and incur no danger whatever." The hope of the reward was too much for the barber's fidelity: he promised the Rani to do as she bade, and, consequently, this morning was making his razor very sharp, rubbing it on the whetstone again and again. The Raja sat silently waiting, when suddenly his eye chanced to light upon the Brahman's verse, and, quite unthinkingly, he read it out.

"Rubbing, rubbing, dipping, then rubbing with might and main;
What your rubbing's all for, is easy enough to explain!"

Hearing these words, the barber was thunderstuck. He stood staring for a moment, then, throwing away the razor, strop and all, he clasped the Raja's feet, and cried, weeping bitterly, "Moharaj, pardon me! I know nothing about it. It was the Rani and the Kotwal bade me. Moharaj, you would not kill a poor man like me!" He was in too great a fright to say any more. The Raja was astounded. He said sternly to the barber, "What is the matter? Tell the truth, and no harm shall happen to you." The barber answered, "Moharaja, this is all I know. Yesterday, Her Majesty sent for me and said, 'Tomorrow, when you are shaving the Raja, if you can manage to cut his throat, I will give you an immense

[3]Shaving, with a Hindu, is an important religious duty. See MWR, pp. 374 f.

reward, and I promise that no harm shall happen to you.' The Kotwal, too, said the the same, for he was standing there at the time. I was enticed by the bribe, and intended to commit the crime. But you have detected all.[4] Pardon me, Your Majesty." The Raja sent away the barber, and then made proclamation throughout the city by beat of drum, that the maker of the verse should be seized and brought before him. The Brahman, on hearing this, was terribly alarmed. "It's all up with me now," he thought. "What I feared has come to pass. The Raja will have my head, to a certainty. That confounded verse!" Presently, the Raja's messengers came and laid hold of him. The Brahman, beside himself with terror, began to say to his wife,

---

[4]Cf. KSS, I, pp. 273 ff. The poor and foolish Brahman, Harisarman, pretends to possess supernatural knowledge. When some gold and jewels are carried off from the palace, he is summoned to detect the thief. Now, the theft had been committed by a maid-servant called Jihva (= Tongue) with the help of her brother. Harisarman, being quite at a loss and much afraid, apostrophizes his own tongue about the trouble its boasting has brought upon him. This leads to Jihva's confession. The Raja, advised by his envious minister, in order to put Harisarman to a further test, places a frog in a pitcher, and, convering it, asks him what it contains. Now, Harisarman's father had called him by the pet name, 'Frog," when he was a child. In his perplexity and despair, he says to himself, "This is a fine pitcher for you, Frog! It has destroyed you." Cf., also, the story of 'Dr. Knowall,' GHT, II, pp. 56 f.
It is just in such cases of what a European would call curious coincidence that an Oriental sees, not chance, but the most striking evidence of Fate's sovereign ordering of events. See KSS, I, p. 402, and II, p. 382.

"Now you've got what you wanted. What with the alms I brought in and suchlike, we were getting along not so badly. But nothing would satisfy you short of my going to the palace, and see now what's come of it!" His wife replied, "What are you weeping for? You've done no crime, that the Raja should cut your head off. Go along to the palace. Let us see what Fate has in store for us." The Brahman again said, "I don't need to go. I know very well already. The Raja will take you and make you his Rani, and will have me impaled. What more would you have?" So saying, and weeping bitterly, the Brahman was brought to the palace. When he saw him, the Raja asked, "Thakur, did you write this verse?" The Brahman, still weeping, answered "Yes, Moharaj." The Raja then said, "You have saved my life. How can I reward you as you deserve? The half of my kingdom is yours." On hearing such words, the Brahman was overjoyed, and the Raja's attendants proceeded at once to make him a Raja too, with all due ceremony. Meanwhile, the Raja had departed to the Rani's residence, where he ordered her and the Kotwal to be beheaded. Thereafter he, with the Brahman and his wife, continued to live together in the greatest happiness and splendour.

V

THE STOLEN WIFE

In a certain village lived a Brahman and a Kayastha, who were very great friends. The Brahman was wretchedly poor, and his old mother and himself made up his entire household. The Kayastha's circumstances were a little better, and several of his relatives were still living. Both were unmarried. One day, the Brahman said to his friend, "Brother, I positively must get married. I can't stand this sort of life any longer. But how am I to raise the money to defray all the expenses of a marriage? And, even if I could, who would be willing to give his daughter to a man so poor as I am?[1]

---

[1]The Brahman could not have belonged to a high class in his caste, otherwise his poverty would have been no obstacle to his procuring a wife, both beautiful and wealthy. Nor would bad character either, for that matter. Dinabandhu Mitra, in his 'Lilavati' describes the Brahman Zemindar as anxious to wed his beautiful, virtuous, and accomplished daughter to an utter wastrel, without one redeeming trait, either outward or inward. Now-a-days, of course, character, education, and the probable ability of the bridegroom to support a wife are looked to, as well as caste, which, however, still remains the supreme consideration. The members of the great Pirali house of the Tagores, which claims to be Radriya Brahman and will intermarry only with that class, when bridegrooms are wanted for their daughters, are willing to pay heavy premiums for them to their families as compensation for the detriment to caste which alliance with a Pirali entails.

All the same, get a wife I must and will." "You're quite right, brother," replied the Kayastha. "And I'm of the very same mind, myself. But there's no chance of our getting wives in this neighbourhood. Let's go and try our luck in some distant village. By hook or by crook, we'll get hold of a couple of girls, and, when we've fetched them home, it'll be easy enough to say we've married them." "But, brother," objected the Brahman, "I see a lot of difficulties about that plan. Whose girls are we to get hold of, and are any likely to be willing to come with us? No, that won't work." "Don't you trouble your head about the business," was the reply. "Just come along with me, and I'll bring you back a married man." "You're promising a deal more than you can perform," said the Brahman. "I'm much more likely to lose my life than to gain a bride by any such adventure." "Look here, brother," answered the Kayastha, "I'll do all the thinking. You'll have only to act as I bid you. And you'll see how soon I'll get you married. But one thing you must promise. After I have spared no pains to find a wife for you, you must in turn do all you can to help me to procure one for myself."[2] "Of course; that goes without saying," replied the Brahman.

The compact made, the two friends waited for an auspicious day,[3] and then set out on their quest. All

[2]Apart altogether from the somewhat unusual character of matrimonial enterprise in the case of these two worthies, a friend's help was a necessity, as, in the matter of marriage, no Hindu can, himself, take any sort of overt action.

[3]So, Suryaprabha marches out to war at a moment on the seventh day fixed by the astrologers—KSS, I, p. 434. See, also, Note 22 in this story.

day, they walked on, and, towards evening, reached a village neither of them had ever visited before. Just outside of it was a fine big tank, to which all the women and girls in the village used to come after sunset to draw water, and bathe, and wash their clothes. Beside it stood a banyan tree, at the foot of which the two friends sat down, and began to view the women going to or coming from the tank. Just then, a very pretty young woman appeared—as pretty as she was young. Taking a good look at her, the Kayastha asked his companion, "Brother, how does that young woman please you?" "Very much indeed," was the reply. "But what does that matter? There's no chance of her becoming my wife." "Just wait and see whether I shan't manage it," answered the Kayastha.

While this consultation was taking place, the young woman, after washing herself and her *sari*,[4] went away back the way she came. Seeing this, the two friends got up and followed her at some distance. On entering the village, she turned off by a side-path, and they sat down in a shop close by, and got into conversation with the shopkeeper. After talking for a while about this and that, while they sat smoking, the Kayastha, in a casual sort of way, asked the shopkeeper, "By the

---

[4]A long piece of cloth—in Bengal, usually, thin white cotton —which Hindu women wind round the body, the one portion forming a petticoat, the other covering the upper part of the person, and, when necessary, the head as well. Even without a bodice, the *sari* discharges the primary function of dress much more efficiently than European "full" evening costume. Cf. CLER, p. 460. See, also, MWR, p. 396.

way, who was the young woman that turned along the lane over there?" The shopkeeper keeper was a talkatiye old fellow. If you asked him one thing, he would tell you half-a-dozen. "Oh, she's a Brahman's daughter," said he. "She's the best-looking girl in the village. But much good that does her. She's been very unfortunate. Immediately after her marriage, her husband went away back to his home, and has never been here since, nor sent any word about himself. We hear that he has got a situation in Ranigunje, and has married and set up house there. To all intents and purposes, he has abandoned his wife here. That's why I said the girl had been very unfortunate." The Kayastha pretended to be very sorry for the poor thing, and inquired, "What relatives has she here?" Her father and mother live here, answered the shopkeeper. "Her father's name is Ramesh'or Chokroborti. He stays quite near here. That's his house, just over yonder. And where are you two gentlemen going?" "Ah, we've a long journey before us," replied the Kayastha. "We intend to stay only the one night here. But, speaking about that young woman, you might tell us her husband's name, and what sort of employment he's in. Likely enough, we shall be passing Ranigunje, and we might take the opportunity of looking him up and trying to persuade him to come and visit his wife here. "Ah, it's easy to see you are born gentlemen," said the shopkeeper. "It's very kind, indeed, of you to think of taking so much trouble. The Babu's name is Ramlochon Mukherji. People say he's a clerk in such-and-such a firm's office."

Having learned this much, after taking another pull at the hookah and thanking the old shopkeeper profusely for his hospitality, the two friends rose and bade him good-evening. As soon as they were outside in the road, the Kayastha said, "The business is as good as done. Come along, let us go to her house." "How can we do that?" asked the Brahman. "It's simple enough," was the reply. "You pass yourself off as Ramesh'or Babu's[5] son-in-law, and I'll be your servant. Now, attend well to what I say. As soon as we enter the house, you must bow respectfully to your father-in-law and mother-in-law. Then, when they ask why you have been so long in visiting them, you must say that you suffered from a long and very severe ill-ness—so severe that you were actually carried down to the Ganges;[6] that, as Fate would have it, you were fortunate enough to recover, contrary to all expectation; but that the effect of the illness has been completely to change your appearance and your voice, so that nobody, seeing you or hearing you speak, would recognize you to be

---

[5]*Babu* denotes any man whose social position is such that he would be addressed or spoken of a "Mr." So-and-so. It is used with the personal, not with the family, name. A European would say, "Mr. Chokroborti;" a Bengali says, "Ramesh'or Babu."

[6]No member of a strict Hindu family is allowed to die inside the house. When death seems imminent, the bed is carried outside, and, very often, a start for the Ganges is made at once. If it is reached in time for the patient to die beside or in the sacred stream, so much the better. Cases of apparently dying people recovering after arriving there, do, of course, sometimes occur.

the same person. Further, you must say, that your mother is dangerously ill—is, in fact, dying; that, as she was living all alone, with nobody in the house to give her even a drink of water, the moment you got news of her being ill, you asked some weeks' leave from your employers, and hurried home; and that, as soon as you arrived, your mother expressed a strong desire to see your wife, who is here. You have, therefore, come at once to fetch her, and must start for home again this very night." The Brahman, with much trepidation, agreed to follow his friend's instructions.

The two walked up to the door of the house, and the Kayastha began to call, "Oh, Chokkotti Moshay,[7] are you in?" The old Brahman had lain down to rest, but, hearing the call, he got up and, opening the door, asked, "Who are you, good people?" "Why, sir," answered the Kayastha, "that's your son-in-law. Don't you recognise him?" the old man, quite overjoyed, cried, "What! Is it you, my dear Ramlochon? Come in, my dear, come in!" The suppsed son-in-law, making a respectful bow to his father-in-law, followed him into the house. The old man called to his wife, who was in the women's part of the house, "Come! Quick! Quick! Quick! Our Ramlochon is come." The old lady came hurrying out, and the Brahman bowed to her very respectlfully, son-in-law fashion. She shed tears of joy.

---

[7]A more respectful mode of address than "Ramesh'or Babu." "Chokkotti Moshay" is the vulgar pronunciation of Chokroborti Mohashoy. The Kayastha has to speak like a servant.

"Oh, my dear!" said she. "Have you at length remembered us after so long? What had we done to displease you that, year after year, you never came near us? And we have no other sons. You are our all." As she spoke, her tears streamed down more and more profusely. "Don't weep, mother," said the impostor. "It's not my fault that I've had to stay away so long. I've been so ill. For months, I was at death's door. Don't you see how sickness has altered me? I'm quite a different man. My very voice is no longer the same." Hearing this, the mother-in-law began very affectionately to condole with him. "May you live long, my dear," said she, by way of comforting him. "In time, you'll get back your good looks. Where there are the bones, the flesh will come of itself." With these words, she went away to cook supper for him and, in order that he might have some refreshment at once the old Brahman hurried to the nearest milkman's and confectioner's, and, knocking them up, got a quantity of milk and *shondesh*.[8] On his way back, he called at a fisherman's, too, and procured a fine big fish, which he gave to his wife to cook, and then set the milk and sweetmeats before his son-in-law and his servant. While they were eating, the daughter was preparing betel for them in the next room. She, too, was overjoyed at the arrival of her husband after so long an absence that she had given up all hope of ever seeing him again. But, taking a peep at him through the venetian door

[8]Made with sugar and fresh curd; the most popular of all Bengali sweets.

between the two rooms, she at once became very suspicious. "That my husband!" said she to herself. "Not a bit of it! Well; let me see what Fate has in store for me."

Presently, the old Brahman returned, and told them that supper had been set out on the clay verandah of the house. Thither they repaired, and when, first, the master with his father-in-law, and, after them, the servant[9] had eaten their fill, the supposed son-in-law, turning to their host, said, "Mohashoy, I haven't yet told you all my misfortunes. My venerable mother is most dangerously ill. It was this news that made me take leave from the office and hurry home. The first words my mother said to me on my arrival, were, 'Fetch her'[10] (*viz.*, his wife) 'at once, else I shall never see her

---

[9]Being of different castes, the Brahman and his man could not, of course, eat *rice* together.

[10]Observe, not merely the personal name but even the word meaning "wife" is avoided. A Bengali usually speaks of his wife as his "*poribar,*" *i.e.*, "family," although referring to her individually.

[11]A son-in-law's visit is regarded as a very joyful event not only for his wife—see the first ch. of Sivanath Sastri's exquisite story, 'Mejo Bou' = 'The Second Daughter-in-law'—but for her whole family. This must certainly have been the case when Kulinism flourished in full vigour. An angel's visits could hardly be "in it," so far as rarity is concerned, with those of some Kulin husbands, who could hardly make the round of all their wives in the course of a lifetime. "A Kulin of a high class might then marry more than a hundred wives without any difficulty, and there are still some who have such large numbers of wives as to necessitate their keeping regular registers for refreshing their memory about the names and residences of their spouses"—J. N. Bhattacharjee, 'Hindu Castes and Sects,' p. 41.

again.' So I hurried off here. I can't wait. You must let your daughter go with me this very night." "What are you saying, my dear fellow?" cried the old man. "You have just arrived, and after all these years too![11] You must stay a few days, and let us have a good time together. The neighbours must have a chance of coming to see you, too. After that, I won't, of course, object to your going and taking your property" (*viz.*, his wife) "with you. But, first, give us time fully to realize our good fortune. Ah, my daughter, who was for so long to all intents and purposes a widow, is now going to keep her husband's house!" "That's all very true," was the reply, "but, in present circumstances, it's absolutely impossible for me to stay. Any minute, my mother may breathe her last, and there's positively no one in the house to do anything for her. You must let your daughter go at once." The old Brahman, though greatly disappointed, had perforce to consent, and went away to hire palki-bearers, whom he brought back along with him,[12] so that his son-in-law might be able to start the moment day broke.

Meanwhile, the supposed son-in-law had gone to his wife's (?) room to rest. The young woman, too, repaired thither, after she had supped. If any doubt that he might be her husband after all had lingered in her mind, it was quite dispelled the moment she got a good look at him close at hand. What was she to do? She had to lie down, but she turned her back to the

[12]This is a quite usual precaution in the Mofussil—the country, as opposed to the town.

Brahman, without saying a single word to him. He coaxed and entreated. It was of no use. Then he began to say, "Is it because my appearance and voice are so altered that you can't bear me? See, I brought a beautiful set of gold ornaments[13] for you from Ranigunje. As soon as we reach home, you'll get them to wear. What's the use of making us both miserable by going on like that?" Not a word could he get out of her. She lay, weeping silently.

When it was near daybreak, the Kayastha, who had slept in the verandah, got up and began loudly to call, "Babu, Babu!" The Brahman rose and went out, and, seeing there was no time to lose, he and his companion began at once to prepare for their departure. Their host was already up and seated on the verandah, and the bearers were sitting beside the palki, smoking and talking noisily. "So you're quite set on going at once?" said the old man to his guest. "Yes, Mohashoy," was the reply. "There's no help for it." The old man rose with a sigh, and called to his daughter to dress quickly, and come away. When she came out, he helped her into the palki. The girl was weeping bitterly. So, too, was her mother. But not much time could be allowed them for leave-taking. The bearers lifted the palki. The Brahman bowed humbly to his father-in-law and mother-in-law, and took up the dust from their feet to his head.[14] Then the palki moved

---

[13]This is believed by Bengali men—not without reason—to be the most effective, nay, an absolutely infallible means of pleasing a Bengali woman.

[14]The obeisance in question symbolizes this. I never saw a man actually take up some dust and put it on his head.

off, the Brahman, followed by his servant, walking alongside.

Once outside the village, the bearers smartened their pace, and it took the two friends all their time not to be left behind. Still, a good deal of whispering went on between them, The Kayastha said to the Brahman, "Well, brother, thanks to me, your business has been satisfactorily accomplished. Now it's your turn to help me. You must promise that, until I've been provided for, you won't live with this girl as your wife. When we get home, you must leave her with your mother, and we'll go off together on a second hunt, till we've secured another young woman. I'll take her, and you'll keep this one. Or, if this proposal does not please you, this one must belong to us both." "No, no," said the Brahman. "That's not to be thought of. I'll help you to find a wife for yourself, as we agreed at the first." The young woman in the palki was listening sharply. Now and again, she managed to catch a word or two of their conversation, and easily divined the rest. Plainly, they were a pair of swindlers. She began fervently to take the name of Bhogoban,[15] for she felt she had no other resource.

Presently, they arrived at a river. The village, to which the Brahman and the Kayastha belonged, was not very far from this spot. The Kayastha said to his companion,

---

[15]Sk., *bhagavan* = adorable, denoting the supreme God, as in 'Bhagavadgita' = the song of the Adorable. Cf. CLER, p. 163, Note, and p. 542.

"We must send away the palki-bearers here. If we take them to our village with us, they'll get to know all about us, and our game'll be up." Then he called to the bearers, "Listen, you fellows. At our house, everything's in confusion with the mistress's being ill. There'll be nobody to cook food for you and make you comfortable till you can start for home again. So, if you go on with us, you'll have no end of trouble and discomfort. Here we can easily get a boat or a carriage to take us home. So we'll give you your full pay and food-money besides, and let you go." The bearers, of course, had no objection to this proposal, and, receiving their money, went off with the palki, leaving the young woman with the two men. She had been coming to see through things more and more clearly in the course of the journey; now, she fully understood the situation and had made up her mind how to act. So, when the two friends said her, "It will be better for you to do just as we wish; you'll only make things worse for yourself by trying to thwart us," she replied at once, "I will do whatever you tell me to; for, since you have brought me away here, now I am yours." Addressing the Brahman, she said, "Though you're not really my husband, I've got to accept you as such, and will obey you in everything." Hearing this, they were greatly delighted, and began to say to one another, "What a Loqhi of a girl! She's as good as she's beautiful. Merely to hear her speak is delightful."

All the time they were talking, they kept walking on

towards their village, where they arrived before long. The Brahman at once went into his house, and said to his mother, "Mother, I've got married and have brought my wife home." Greatly excited at this news, the old Brahmani cried out joyfully, "Where is she, my dear? Where is she?" The supposed bride at once came forward and bowed humbly to her mother-in-law, who, lifting up her hands, began to bless her fervently. "Come, my dear," she said, "my Loqhi, my golden moon![16] Long may you live! May your bracelet have plenty of time to wear out. When your head is hoary, may it still bear the vermilion mark. May you have a husband all your life,"[17] and so forth. One by one, the other women of that part of the village came dropping in to see the new wife, and the old Brahmani showed her off with great pride and delight. All admired her beauty, and congratulated her mother-in-law on her good fortune in being gladdened at her time of life with the sight of such a daughter. "Bride's no name for her," they said. "She's a statue of pure gold." The bride bowed humbly to them all, and spoke to them in the most mannerly fashion. And the old woman begged them to give her son and his wife their blessing, wishing the latter a long life as mistress of her husband's house.

---

[16]A very common expression of endearment.

[17]The iron bracelet, put on at marriage, is broken off when a woman becomes a widow, and she ceases to mark her brow where the hair parts, with the round scarlet spot, the sign that a woman is married and her husband still living.

She, herself, she said, didn't care how soon she died, now that she had seen her son happily married. After much talk of this kind, the visitors departed to their own homes. But they were hardly outside the old Brahmani's door before they began to whisper to one another, "What sort of a wedding is this? People turning up all of a sudeen, married! She's none that young either. Why wasn't she married long ago! And how's he to support her when he hasn't the means of keeping his own stomach going? Who can have been fools enough to give their daughter to the like of him?"

Anyhow, one thing soon became plain, and that was that the new bride was a model daughter-in-law. She rose early in the morning, and cleaned and tidied up the house. Then she awakened her mother-in-law, rubbed her with oil, helped her to bathe, and washed for her the *sari* she put off. She brought her dainties from the confectioner's.[18] She did all the cooking, and would not touch food, herself, till she had given her

---

[18]To serve as light refreshments to sustain fainting nature till regular meal-time, *i.e.,* the time when she got her rice. According to Medhatithi's explanation of Manu, II, 56, such eating "between-times" is forbidden. This seems rather hard, as nothing could be more irregular than the "regular meals" in an old-fashioned Bengali household. School-hours generally begin at 10.30 a. m., yet boys have often to be allowed to go home after the first or second period to take breakfast, which was not ready when they had to leave in the morning. A mother will awake small children between 10 and 11 p.m., to give them their evening meal. A man may be invited to an evening-meal party, and, if it is a very big affair, it may be 1 or 2 a.m. next morning before the dishes are served up.

mother-in-law her breakfast. The latter never tired of congratulating herself and praising her daughter-in-law.

In this way, a week or two passed—not very pleasantly for the Brahman. According to the compact made with his friend, he was debarred from even so much as speaking to his wife, until one had been got for him too. And, night and day, the Kayastha kept urging him, "Come away, brother, and get a marriage for me fixed up. Till then, you might as well be unmarried, yourself." The Brahman was very unwilling to go, but, knowing that the other had him in his power, and at any moment could ruin him by disclosing his secret, at length, one day, he said, "Well, then, come away. Though it's so long since I brought my wife home all this time, on your account, I haven't been able to say a single word to her. I'm sick of this sort of thing." "Then the sooner we start, the better," was the reply. "Very good," rejoined the Brahman. "Let us start this very day.' So it was arranged they should leave as soon as they had breakfasted.

The Brahman had now full confidence in his wife. Besides, he couldn't see what she had to gain by trying to escape. Where was she to go? So, handing over to her the keys of all his chests, he said to her, "See; until I've arranged a marriage for my friend, I can have no sort of intimacy with you. So I'm going off to-day to attend to that business. I don't know how long I may be in returning. I leave my mother in your care. I know you'll be as good to her as you can. I need say no more." "No," said she, "you may trust me to do all you would wish. She's now as much my mother as yours. So I'm not likely to show her any neglect. You can see for yourself whether I've been in any way wanting in my duty to her since I came here. And it's your duty to do all you can to get your friend married. You would be guilty of a great sin if you didn't. Remember how much trouble he took in connexion with your marriage. It would be a shame for you to delay an hour longer. And don't be anxious about your household affairs. I'll keep everything right." Hearing her speak in this way, the Brahman was quite overcome. If any doubt as to her fidelity still lingered in his breast, it was now completely dispelled. So, leaving everything in her charge, with a perfectly easy mind, he took his departure along with his friend.

For two or three days, the young woman continued to show the old Brahmnani every possible attention, and contrived, without rousing any suspicious, to find out from her what valuables there were in the house, and where they were kept. Indeed, this was easy enough, as the old woman talked quite freely about everything. Then, one night, having given her the light meal she took in the evening,[19] she put her to bed. Waiting till she as sound asleep, the young woman proceeded to gather together all the things that were worth taking away, and tied them up in a bundle. Then, locking the door from the outside, she set fire to the house and made off as fast as ever she could. In a very

[19]Being a widow, she could take only one "square" meal of rice, etc., in the day.

few minutes, she had left the village behind, and found herself in the midst of a wide plain. In what directioin was she to go now? "What I had to do, I've done," she said to herself. "Bhogoban has gaciously preserved my honour this time, but, if I'm caught again, it'll be all up with me. If I only knew what way to go! But it won't do to stand still here." So thinking, she fervently called Bhogoban to mind,[20] and then walked straight on in one direction all that night. At daybreak, suddenly she saw that she was close to the tank where she used to come to bathe and wash her clothes. Her joy at the sight was unbounded. Tired as she was, she ran all the rest of the way home. Her parents were greatly astonished to see her—above all, to see her alone. "Where is our son-in-law?" asked her mother. "How in the world could he let you come by yourself?" "Oh, I haven't come alone," she answered. "Yesterday my mother-in-la died, and my husband has to go with her body to the Ganges. Rather than leave me all by myself in his house, he came round this way and left me here. Seeing he was conveying a corpse, he would not come to the house with me or wait to see you."[21] The old Brahman and his wife were greatly concerned to hear such bad news. "Ah," said her mother, "to think that your mother-in-law should have died so soon after you went home with your husband! Dear knows what

---

[20]Hindus regard "remembering"—Sk., *smarana*—as a means of positively compelling the saving presence of a god.

[21]To avoid bringing ceremonial defilement upon them. See MWR, p. 285.

people will say about you. And she was the only relative our son-in-law had with him in his house. Anyhow, you're our daughter, and it was better to bring you here than leave you in an empty house. It's a joy to us to have you with us." Never for a moment doubting the truth of their daughter's explanations, the old people made no further inquiries, and their daughter stayed on with them just as before her supposed husband's visit.

Meanwhile, the Brahman and the Kayastha had been wandering from village to village, but not the smallest success attended their efforts. At last, the Kayastha said, "It was at an auspicious moment that we set out the first time. This time, we must have started at a most inauspicious one.[22] We're doing no good anywhere. Everywhere, something turns up to baulk us. I'm sick of this. Let's go home, and make a fresh start when we've ascertained a lucky day and hour for doing so." The Brahman was only too glad to assent.

The morning after the young woman fled, when the villagers rose, they saw that the Brahman's house had

---

[22]Cf. the following. The five confederate kings march against Chamarabala, in spite of the astrologers' declaration that there would be no favourable moment that year for commencing a campaign, and are routed by an army not more than a quarter as large as their own—KSS, I, pp. 532, 535. By starting on a journey in spite of bad omens, the Brahman youth, Vishnudatta's, seven companions nearly lose their lives—*ib.*, I, pp. 283 ff. The result of King Ratnadhipati's marrying Rajadatta at a time declared inauspicious by the astrologers, is that she proves unfaithful to him, precisely as they forewarn him—KSS, I, pp. 330 ff.

been burned to the ground during the night. The women, supposing she and her mother-in-law had perished together,[23] began to lament the bride. "Alas!" said they, "where in all the village was there another young wife like her? To think of her coming to such an end, and so soon! Why, it was just the other day her husband brought her home; and for this! What will he say when he returns?" They were standing, gazing at the ruins and talking in this strain, when the two friends arrived on the scene. When the Brahman saw the blackened remains of his house and realized what had befallen him, he was almost beside himself with grief and remorse. "Ah," said he to himself, "I've reaped what I sowed. This is that accursed creature's doing. Well, robbery has been perpetrated on the robber."[24] The Kayastha, who was standing by, said, "Brother, I'm for no more work of this kind. I've got my eyes opened." Saying this, he went away.

The Brahman thought to himself, "What's the use of my staying here? Rather let me see whether I can't give that wretch of a woman a lesson." So, tying a short cloth round his neck,[25] he took the road to her village. All day, he walked straight on, not stopping

---

[23]With the success of the "stolen wife's" artifice, cf. KSS I, p. 61. Sridatta conveys a woman and her daughter into the palace, makes them drunk, fires the palace, and carries off the Princess Mrigankavati and her companion. Everybody supposes that it is they that have perished.

[24]A favourite Bengali proverb.

[25]This is done by a son when father or mother dies.

even once to rest, and, towards evening, arrived at Ramesh'or Babu's house. Stopping at the gate, he called out, "Oh, Chokroborti Mohashoy, Chokroborti Mohashoy! are you in?" The old Brahman was sitting in his verandah. He at once ran to the gate, and, seeing his supposed son-in-law, cried, "Oh, is it you, my dear Ramlochon? Come away in! Come away in! I've heard all, and am greatly grieved to know that your mother is gone. You did very right to send your wife here; very right!" Saying this, he grasped his son-in-law's hand and led him into the house. The old Brahmani wept when she saw him, and then went on to say, "But don't grieve, my dear! Who can have his mother and father with him all his life? Her time had come, and she's gone. Grieving won't do any good. She was very fortunate to leave a son like you behind her. I'm sure my husband and I shall be glad to die, leaving you and our daughter behind us." After talking in this strain for a while, the old Brahmani went away to see about some refreshment for him, and her husband, just as on the former occasion, hurried to this and the other shop to fetch things. Their guest thought to himself, "So far good. She seems to have revealed nothing when she got home. The two old folks are still quite in the dark. Well, only let me manage to get her away with me again, and I'll let her see."

Meanwhile, the daughter was saying to herself, "It's all up with me! The villain has come back! He'll be wishing to take me away at once, and my parents will insist on my going. What on earth am I to do?" Suddenly an idea struck her, and, going quickly to the back of the house, she called an old woman, who stayed there. "Grannie," said she, "you'd be doing me a great kindness, if you'd get me some poison." "Poison, child!" replied the old woman, "what can you want poison for?" "Oh," said she, "our house is overrun with mice. They're spoiling everything we have. I'll mix the poison with some food, and put it down in my room. In that way, some of the vermin at least will be got rid of." "Yes, that's quite true," answered the old woman, and, going to the bazar, she presetly came back with some poison, which she handed to the young woman. The refreshments had by this time been got ready, and the old Brahmani, sending a maid-servant with them to her daughter's room, said to her son-in-law, "You won't, of course, wish to take rice to-night,[26] but I've sent some food for you to your wife's room. You'd better eat something, and then go early to bed, as you must be very tired after such a busy and trying day." He thanked her, and then, turning to her husband, said, "Mohashoy, will you be so good as to make an arrangement with some palki-bearers to-night. I must set out with my wife at daybreak. As you know, there's nobody at all in my house now." "Certainly I will," was the reply. "Leave all that to me. Now, do you go and

[26]In consequence of his mother's death, he could take only one proper meal in the day until the *sraddha* should be celebrated, and she assumed that he had breakfasted somewhere.

rest, my dear fellow."

Bidding the old couple good-night, the Brahman betook himself to the daughter's room, where he found her sitting waiting for him. Almost paralyzed with terror as she was, she had pulled herself together sufficiently to mix the poison with the glass of milk which had been set ready for him. The Brahman had had nothing to eat or drink all day. Being parched with thirst, he took up the glass of milk and drank it off at one draught. He had hardly set down the empty glass, when he began to foam at the mouth, and fell writhing on the floor. In a few seconds he was dead.

"That's one thing accomplished," thought the young woman to herself. "But what am I to do with the corpse? If it's found here in the morning, I shall be dragged straight off to jail. I can't tell my parents. Yet how am I to dispose of it by myself? Well, let me see once more what Bhogoban will do for me?" She sat, thinking hard, and, before long, what seemed a feasible plan occurred to her. She rose, and put on all her ornaments; then, from amongst her *saris,* picking out a splendid scarlet silk one, she wrapped it about her. Also, she ate some betel,[27] and unfastened her hair, which hung down past

---

[27]Bengali, *pan-shupari. Pan* is the leaf of the *Piper Betel, shupari,* the Areca nut. A little piece of the latter, pounded small, is wrapped up along with moist lime and various spices inside the leaf, the whole being pinned together in triangle shape with a clove. This forms "*a pan.*" On great occasions, it is covered with gold leaf. The immediate effect of eating *pan* is to dye the saliva blood-red. The lips, gums, tongue, etc., of habitual eaters of large quantities of *pan,* are always of a very bright scarlet hue.

her waist. The corpse she tied up firmly in one of her old *saris*. Then, waiting till everybody in the house was certain to be sound asleep, by exerting all her strength, she succeeded in lifting the corpse upon her head, and, taking in her hand an old scimitar, which happened to be lying in her room, she made her way out. Not very far off, there was a cemetery.[28] Thither she wended her way as fast as she could. When she reached the place, it was the very dead of night. The chirping of the crickets seemed piercingly loud. The sky was overclouded, but, now and again, a flash of lightning lit up the inky darkness and a big drop of rain fell. Now, a band of robbers happened to be sitting in the cemetery, planning together their next expedition.[29] The woman would have walked straight in among them,

---

[28]Place where corpses are cremated, generally beside a stream or tank.

[29]Such places figure in Indian Tales as a favourite night-haunt of robbers. Cf. LDB, p. 170; CLER, p. 133. If they chanced to see a corpse on the left hand, when entering, that was a good omen. And, in such a place during the night, they were safe from disturbance by human beings. One has to remember how a cemetery appeared to the Hindu *imagination.* "It was obscured by a dence and terrible pall of darkness, and its aspect was rendered awful by the ghastly flames fromthe burning of the funeral pyres, and it produced horror by the bones, skeletons, and skulls of men that appeared in it. In it were present formidable Bhutas and Vetalas, joyfully engaged in their horrible activity (of devouring corpses), and it was alive with the loud yells of jackals—KSS, II p. 233 of. p. 387; also, the Introduction to the *Vetalapanchavinsati* or 'Vikram and the Vampire.' Robbers, as special favourites of Kali, would, of course, feel quite secure.

but, luckily, when she was still some little way off, a flash of lighting revealed them to her. They, of course, were too busily occupied to notice her. She stopped short, shaking with sudden terror. "Ah," she thought to herself, "after committing so many crimes to preserve my honour[30] and my life, I'm doomed to lose both at the hand of those robbers. Well, I must do my best to save myself." Calling to mind Bhogoban, and, quickly adapting her original plan to these unforeseen circumstances, she walked on straight towards the robbers. The tinkle of her anklets, suddenly falling on their ears, made them aware that a woman was approaching. But what woman could be coming to such a place on such a night—and at the very dead of night too? And what could bring her? They were consulting

---

[30]Excepting the theft from the impostor-husband's house, with which the story seems to blemish the character of the heroine quite unnecessarily, the exceptional means she used to preserve her chastity, and, with it, her caste and the honour of the real husband, who had treated her so badly, would be all but condoned by strict, old-fashioned Hinduism; just as a very ancient Israelite, no doubt, regarded as proofs of heroic self-devotion the extraordinary steps taken by Tamar and the daughters of Lot to secure the supremely important end of the perpetuation of their families.

The Hindu estimate of the preciousness and power of chastity is illustrated in such stories as that of the Water-Genius, KSS, II, p. 82. On his wife's praying and appealing by her chastity that her husband may no longer have to dwell in the water, an aerial chariot appears and carries them both to heaven. Damayanti, when abandoned in the forest by Nala, is in danger of suffering violence at the hands of a hunter. Appealing to her chastity, she successfully imprecates instant death upon him—MBH, Vana P., LXIII.

together thus in whispers, when she came close up to them, stood stock-still, put out her bloody-looking tongue,[31] and held up the scimitar. The robbers hurriedly lit a torch, and, the moment they were able to see the strange apparition plainly, they concluded for certain it was Mother Kali, herself. All robbers, as is well known, are devout worshippers of the goddess.[32] So the whole band, making the most humble obeisance, began to worship the young woman. Their captain, falling at her feet again and again, said to her, "Mother, if we gain much booty on to-night's expedition, I'll get a tongue of gold made, and delicate it to you, and it'll have your *puja* celebrated with great splendour." And all of them, shouting "Victory to the Mother! Victory

---

[31]The effect of the betel. When Kali was slaughtering the demons, she waxed so furious that the earth was like to give way under her tread. The gods having failed to stop her by any other means, Siva went and lay down in her path on the battlefield. Before she was aware, she trod upon her husband, and, when she discovered it, protruded her tongue through shame. She is commonly represented in this attitude. See MWR, p. 189, with Note. Cf. the votive offering the captain promises below. It was certainly an article more in character than the small gold boy the merchant vows to St. Joseph in GOS, I, p. 103.

[32]Thuggee was a notable illustration of this. Essentially, it was a cult of Kali. The plunder was merely the reward bestowed by the goddess upon her votaries in acknowledgment of their zeal in providing human sacrifices for her. The sex of their tutelary deity made it contrary to Thuggee principles to murder women.

On what pleases a deity like Kali, see FOD, p. 325, Not on p. 106. Also, Burke's remarks anent the alleged erection of a temple to Hastings at Benares.

to the Mother!" began to walk round and round her.[33] When they stopped, she said to them, "Children, I am much pleased with you, and have, therefore, brought you this gift. But you must wait a little before you open it." Saying this, she threw down before them the burden she was carrying on her head, and departed. Once clear of the cemetery, she ran home with all the sped she could.

The robbers sat gazing at the bundle she had left, and said to one another, "Now we shall be able to give up this toilsome and dangerous business of robbery. With the reward the Lady of the unbound tresses[34] has bestowed upon us, we shall live at ease for the rest of our lives." Again and again, the captain, his voice trembling with devout emotion, made the sky and the infernal world, itself, resound with his shouts of "Victory to Kali! Victory to Kali!" All the band were wild with joy, picturing to themselves the gold and priceless gems which the bundle, no doubt, contained. After a while,

---

[33]See MWR, p. 334, and Art., "Circumambulation," in Hastings' 'Enc. of Rel. and Eth.' Circumambulation of the sacred fire it part of the Hindu marriage ceremony. MWR, p. 380. Cf. KSS, I, pp. 95 and 98 f. The Brahman, Phalabhuti, by circumambulating a peepul-tree, and making offerings to it, obtains prosperity through the Yaksha that presides over it—*ib.*, I, p. 248. The celestial nymph, Tiolttama, circumambulated Siva, and so beautiful was she that the god became four-faced in order to see her all the time—*ib.*, I, p. 108. Cf. *ib.*, II, pp. 365, 447 and 442. According to the Pseudo-Matth., ch. xii, Mary circumambulated the altar seven times, when subjected to the ordeal of jealousy.

[34]Sk., *Muktakesi*—one of the names of Kali.

the captain gave them leave to open it. When the corpse was revealed to their eager gaze, their anger and disgust knew no bounds[35] The captain fairly shook with rage. "Who can have dared to play such a trick upon me of all people?" he cried. "No doubt, she's some abandoned slut! We must seek her out once. Cutting her in pieces'll be too light a punishment for actually making fools of us!" Saying this, he ordered his men to take up their weapons and follow him, and they, no less eager than himself, seizing their swords, scimitars, spears, and what-not, hurried after him on the road to the village. There, they carefully examined house after house, but could see nothing that looked in any way suspicious. Coming at length to Ramesh'or Babu's house, they sprang one by one over the wall of the courtyard, and found the house-door standing open. The young woman, flurried and worn out with her exertions, had forgotten to close and fasten it. Reaching her own room, she had thrown herself down on her bed and fallen asleep, just as she was. The robbers, entering the house, found their way to her room, and there she lay, still attired in the red *sari* and golden ornaments, with the scimitar, which had slipped from her fingers, on the bed beside her. "Ah," said the captain softly, "we've caught our bird." Then he ordered four of his men to take her up bed and all,[36]

[35]Seeing a corpse in certain circumstances might be a good omen but getting the present of one instead of what they expected, was another matter.

[36]So, in the story of 'The Bed,' the thieves carry off the King's daughter—SIF, p. 206.

and carry her off as gently and quietly as possible, forbidding them on any account to stop and set her down, till they reached the cemetery. The four ruffians, seizing the legs of the bed, carried it noiselessly through the house, and were soon outside the village and well upon their way. So soundly was the young woman sleeping, that it was some time before the jolting of her bed awoke her. When she did awake, and realized that she was being borne rapidly along, she was at a loss to make out what had happened, till, hearing the harsh voices of the robbers on all sides, she became aware that she had fallen into their hands. "It's all up with me now," thought she to herself. "Unless Bhogoban himself delivers me, I'm done for." Just then, the bearers passed under a huge peepul tree, and she felt the twigs brush violently against her body. Straightway, picking up the scimitar, she seized a stout branch and swung herself as gently as possible into the tree. The bed was too heavy of itself for the bearers to notice the difference in its weight, and the darkness hid her movements from the others. Feeling about in the free, she came upon a big hollow in the trunk, which she at once got into.

The robbers soon reached the cemetery, and, setting down the bed, saw to their amazement that its occupant was gone. The captain gnashed his teeth with rage. "Where is the woman?" he fiercely demanded of the bearers. "Master, how can we tell?" answered they. "We took up the bed on our shoulders in the house, and we've set it down here. All the time, between, we noticed nothing whatever. "Perdition!" raved the captain. "To be tricked again and again by one wretched woman! But tell me: did you pass below any trees on your way here?" "Yes," was the reply. "Plenty of them." "Ah, but I mean any very big tree?" said he. "Yes," hey answered, "there was one huge tree." "Then, sure enough, she's climbed up there," cried the captain. "There's nothing she's not fit to do. Do you think you could find your way back to the village by the very same road as you took, coming here?" "Certainly," answered the bearers. "Then carry me back by that road," said the captain. With these words, he lay down on the bed, which the bearers at once too up, and set off towards the village. Presently, the captain felt twigs and leaves brushing against him, and at once called out, "Set me down, set me down! This is the tree. She's bound to be here." Standing at the foot of it, he made his men climb up. They searched all over it, but in vain. No trace of the woman was to be found. Meanwhile, she was crouching in the hollow, almost dead with fear, as she listened to the noise made by the robbers moving hither and thither among the branches. "I can't hope to escape a third time," she thought. "Another minute, and they'll have me. Well, what Bhogoban wills, must be." One by one, the robbers descended, unsuccessful, to where the captain was standing, and, furious at being disappointed, began loudly to complain that he had misled them. The last one of all happened to thrust his hand into the hollow, and, feeling the woman's body, was on the point of joyfully proclaimkng his discovery, when she clapped her hand over his mouth, over his mouth, and said, "Don't call!

What'll you gain by betraying me? Whereas it'll be to your very great profit to do as I tell you." "What do you mean?" asked the robber wonderingly. "Why," was the reply, "if you betray me, the captain, himself, will take possession of me, and you'll have your labour for your pains. But, if you keep quiet, I'll marry you, and we'll live happily together." "Bah!" replied the robber. "Who, do you think, is going to put so much confidence in a wicked woman like you? Besides, I'm not of your caste. How could you marry me, even if you wished it?" "You're a great fool," she rejoined. "What has caste to do with marriage? Here have I put myself in your hands, and you begin gabbling about caste! However, if you won't believe me, you may break my caste here and now. Lean towards me and put out your tongue."[37] Now quite convinced that she really meant to keep her promise, the robber gladly did as she told him, whereupon, as quick, as thought, she seized hold of his tongue with her left hand, and cut off the bigger half of it with the scimitar she held in her right.[38] The robber fell with a crash to the ground, and rolled over and over in agony, choking

[37]Giving him to understand that she would touch his tongue with her own and thereby break her caste.

[38]With this incident, cf. KSS, I, p. 88 and Note. The cunning Siddhikari steals her master's hoarded gold and flees to the jungle. When she sees the merchant and his servants arrive in pursuit of her, she climbs a banyan tree. One of the servants ascends to see if she is there. She makes love to him, and, pretending to wish to kiss him, bites off his tongue with the same result as here. Cf., also, the curious story how the Christian virgin saved her honour, when delivered to the Roman soldier—Liebrecht, 'Zur Volkskunde,' p. 83.

and groaning. The rest of the band, convinced that the tree must be inhabited by some terrible *bhut,*[39] which had done their comrade a deadly hurt, fled in wild panic in all directions. The young woman waited till the sound of their footsteps had died away in the distance, then quietly descended from the tree, and made her way home. Arrived there, she went and lay down in her

---

[39]Demon or goblin; strictly, the ghost of a dead person.
On the subject of haunted trees, see MWR, p. 331, MCF, p. 115, and, for some examples, LDB, pp. 201, 203, and 258; also, KSS, II, p. 365. On the special likelihood that the peepul—Sk., *asvattha, Ficus Religiosa*—might be haunted, see MWR, pp. 335 f; also, KSS, I, p. 153 f. I once preached and showed Bible pictures with the magic-lantern under a peepul, affirmed by the villagers to be the abode of a But. The audience complained that one big branch obstructed their view badly. "Cut it off then," I replied. "*We* daren't, said they. "*You* may, if you like." A bill-hook was brought, and one of my people lopped the branch. When leaving, I asked the villagers whether they weren't afraid the Bhut might pay them out. "Oh, no!" was the reply. "He knows very well that, if you wished to cut his tree, people like us couldn't hinder you. And he won't meddle with you, as he doesn't know what might happen." The leaves of the peepul quiver—like those of the aspen—with the slightest breath of air, hence often move and rustle, when those of all other trees are still. This is irrefragable, palpable evidence that a Bhut is there. On still days, little sporadic puffs of wind seem often to travel about. A whirling column of dust scurries along the road, or the lofty top of a palmyra gives a sudden rattle. Bhuts, to a certainty! I have known cases of a man's turning back instead of going on to do his work, because a tree-top suddenly stirred on a quiet evening.
Some idea of how the robbers pictured to themselves the tenant of the peepul, may be got from KSS, II, p. 338. "At that moment, there suddenly came there a Brahman demon, black as soot, with

own room. Before long, day broke. Everybody in the house rose and began to move about. Seeing their daughter all alone, the old people asked, "Where is our son-in-law? he gave us to believe that he was resolved to take you away with him. What's become of him?" "Oh," said she, "I managed to persuade him to let me remain this time. So he went of very early, promising soon to return for me." Her parents were quite satisfied with this explanation, and their daughter continued to live happily with them as before.

---

hair yellow as the lightning, looking like a thunder-cloud. He had made himself a wreath of entrails; he wore a sacrificial cord of hair; he was gnawing the flesh of a man's head, and drinking blood out of a skull. The monster, terrible with projecting tusks, uttered a horrible, loud laugh, and, vomiting fire with rage, menaced the king in the following words, 'Villain! Know that this *asvattha* (peepul) tree, my dwelling, is not trespassed upon even by gods.'"

VI

NEPHEW KANAI[1]

In a certain country, there lived a Brahman and his wife. The Brahman had some little landed property, and, by laboriously spending his days from morning to night in watching his servants at work in the fields, had scraped together a little money. But his wife was a very wicked woman, who had a lover, and, whatever earnings of her husband she could lay hands on, she spent in buying dainties for her lover. She gave the poor Brahman no end of trouble. At noon, when he came in from the fields, she gave him the very poorest food to eat, and, very often, a volley of abuse along with it. The Brahman was old and had no relatives staying with him, so he had to put up with his wife's tantrums as best he could.

Now the Brahman was a very devout worshipper of Vishnu, and, in spite of all his afflictions, his zeal never abated. He continually invoked him, calling "Narayon, Narayon!"[2] Narayon loves his devotees. He clould not bear to see the pious Brahman's misery. So, taking

---

[1]Colloquial corruption of the name Krishna.

[2]Sk., *Narayana.* Now, one of the names of Vishnu. Cf. LDB, p. 53 f.—the 'Indigent Brahman' constantly repeated the name of Durga.

the form of his nephew, he came to his house. Seeing him come, the Brahman said, "Welcome, my dear! I'm an old man, I'm past working. If you won't take a little trouble to look after me, who will?" The nephew answered, "It is just for that I've come, uncle. I'll stay a long time. You shall have no more trouble." From that day, the nephew would not allow the Brahman to do any work; if his uncle needed to go to the fields, he would go, himself, and let the Brahman remain sitting comfortably at home.

One day, when he came in, he saw that his uncle had not yet bathed. He asked, in surprise, what had hindered him. The Brahman said, "Child, I could get no oil. I asked your aunt for it, but she said there was none." The nephew answered, "What?" and, going straight into the house, he brought out the fine oil which the Brahman's wife had put away to keep for her lover, and anointed and bathed the old man. This done, the nephew called to his aunt, "Aunt, bring my uncle's rice." She brought some coarse rice and sorry vegetables in a common plate, and set them before the Brahman. But the nephew, as soon as he saw this, cried, "Why bring such rice as that, aunt? My uncle can't eat that stuff. I'll eat it, myself." And, going quickly to her room, he found some fine rice, which he brought to his uncle.

The old Brahman that day dined to his heart's content. But his wife, who had been keeping that rice for her lover, gnashed her teeth with rage when she saw her husband eating it. However, it could not be helped, and, indeed, she could not well say anything.

Things went on in this way for some time, when, one day, the nephew brought home some rare dainties for his uncle. His aunt saw them, and determined that, by hook or crook, her lover should get some to eat. So she sent for him and said, "In our house, there is a large clothes' basket. Remain you inside of it,[3] and, at night, I shall give you some delicious food." He agreed, and, that night, the Brahman's wife fed him as she had promised, but so watchful was the nephew that she could not get her lover out of the house. In the morning, the nephew said to her: "Aunt, there must be a very big mouse in that clothes' basket. It kept moving about the whole night. I will kill it." Saying this, he brought the basket, and, lifting it high up, dashed it violently upon the ground. The man fell out, and slunk away home, badly bruised. The Brahman's wife had to look on and say nothing, though choking with rage.

Another day, the nephew again brought home some good things for his uncle. As before, his aunt sent to her lover, saying, "Come to-day. I'll wrap you up out of sight in a mat." But he refused. She sent again, assuring him there was no danger, and, last he consented,and duly turned up at night fall , when she wrapped him up in a mat. During the night she gave him food; but the nephew was aware of what went on. In the morning, he took up the mat and threw it down in the court, and began to beat it with a stick with all

---

[3]Cf. KSS, I, 18 ff. Upakosa stows away her four we lovers in a trunk. See, also, GHT, I, pp. 266 f. and II, pp.

his might. The man inside had terrible mauling, but did not dare to show himself. At last, when the nephew went away, he managed to sneak off. The Brahman's wife saw all this, but she was helpless. All she could do was to abuse the nephew in her heart.

Some time after,he again brought home some great dainties, and the Brahman's wife, as before, sent for her lover, that she might give them to him. He came, but refused to stay. She said: "Don't be afraid. Remain you to-day where I keep the fire-wood. I'll put some pieces of wood on the top of you, and, in that way, you'll be perfectly safe from him. The burnt-faced scoundrel won't come into the kitchen. There I'll feed you, and then let you go, safe and sound." At length he yielded, and the Brahman's wife concealed him as she had promised. The nephew knew it all. Was he not Krishna,[4] the heart-knower? So he came to the kitchen, and said to his aunt: "Aunt, how is there no wood in your scullery? let me fetch you some." His aunt answered: "No, no, child, I don't need wood. Go to your own work. There's plenty of wood in my scullery." But the nephew, never heeding her, brought a huge load of wood, and, flinging it into the scullery upon the man's shoulders, went away. Seeing this, the Brahman's wife extricated him as fast as she could, but he was almost crushed to death by the wood. She did her best to revive him; and, after a while, he was

[4]Krishna is by far the most important *avatara* or incarnation of Vishnu, practically equivalent, indeed, to Vishnu himself, *i.e.,* for a Vaishnava, to the Supreme Being who is the All.

able to slink away home.

Another time, the nephew came in with a great big fish. Again his aunt called her lover, and said, "Remain you to-day in the ditch at the back of my kitchen, and I will pour out the fish along with the rice-water through the drain-hole, so that you may get it all." he agreed, and went and took his seat whee she told him. The Brahman's wife, having boiled her rice, set it to cool. But Krishna, of course, knew what she was after. Coming into the kitchen, he said, "Aunt, why is your pot full of dirty water?" and forthwith poured out the boiling water off the rice through the drain-hole. The man, who was sitting below, got the whole of it upon his face and body, and was horribly scalded. He ran away home, almost beside himself with pain. The Brahman's wife looked on, furious with rage. Thereafter,she did everything in her power to get the nephew sent home. But he put off his departure from day to day, saying, "I'll go to-morrow, will go to-morrow."

One day, the old Brahman said to his nephew, "Child, every since you came, I've been very happy. I've had no trouble at all. But it's long since I celebrated my dead father's feast-ceremony.[5] If you were to make the preparations, I would do so now." The nephew answered, "Don't let that matter trouble you, uncle. I'll make all the arrangements, and you shall celebrate the feast-ceremony." The old Brahman, greatly pleased, lifted up

[5]*Sraddha.* See MWR, pp. 303 ff.

both his hands and blessed his nephew. Thereafter, an auspicious day having been ascertained, Krishna made everything ready. Twelve[6] Brahmans were invited—among them, the lover of the Brahman's wife. They all sat down to eat, he with the rest. Krishna carried round the dishes. When he was about to take round something specially nice, the Brahman's wife called him, and, pointing out her lover, said, "See, child, that Brahman sitting there is a very poor man; give him this little bit extra." The nephew said, "Very good," and, passing through the midst of the others till he was close to that Brahman, he said, "Were you inside the clothes' basket?" He answered, "Not I," whereupon Krishna came back and said, "Aunt, he won't take any." Hearing this, the old Brahman's wife said, "Go again; make him take this titbit." Krishna went up to him as before, and asked, "Were you inside the mat?" He answered, "No, no, not I." Krishna, coming back, and, "Aunt, he won't eat this either." The Brahman's wife began to shake with rage. She said, "If he won't eat this piece willingly, thrust it down his throat." Krishna, as before, went up to him and asked, "Were you among the wood?" He answered "No, no, no, not I." Krishna, coming back to his aunt, said, "He won't eat; what can I do? Whenever I ask whether he'll take anything, just hear how he keeps saying, 'No, no, no, not I.'"[7] The Brahman's wife could say no more,

---

[6]Twelve is what is called a "sacred number." Its special importance is probably derived from the number of the Zodiacal signs, as that of seven is from the number of the principal planets.

[7]Literally translated, the Bengali = Not I, not I, not I. Such threefold asseveration is equivalent to the most solemn possible oath.

and that Brahman go a very poor dinner.

When all the guests were gone, Krishna called the Brahman, and said, "Uncle, further concealment is needless; look well now who I am." Saying this, he manifested himself to the Brahman, in his four-armed form,[8] holding his shell,[9] and discus,[10] and club,[11] and lotus.[12] The Brahman, beholding the theophany of Narayon, putting his upper garment round his neck, began to chant a hymn of adoration. Then Narayon, having burnt up the woman, house and all, took the Brahman by the hand, and led him away to heaven.[13]

---

[8]Sk., *Chatur-bhuja.*

[9]Sk., *Sankha* = a conch.

[10]Sk., *Chakra* = a sort of quoit, used as a weapon.

[11]Sk., *Gada.*

[12]Sk., *Padma.* These four are the best known of Vishnu's insignia. Brahma is the creator, Vishnu the preserver, and Siva the destroyer. But, for a Vaishnava, all three are simply forms or states of Vishnu himself, just as, for a Saiva, they are forms or states of Siva.

[13]Cf. KSS, II, p. 483.

[Nephew Kanai, the name of the hero of this story, is the current designation for a very clever, unscrupulous fellow—one who is able, if offended, to give, in Bengali phrase, "a good lesson," and who has no conscience to keep him from doing so.]